Niroga, Fla. at Lake Yale, Feb. 1982

# Mama's Kitchen Window

D1160129

# Mama's
# Kitchen Window

Vignettes from Life in the Kentucky Hills

by

Alice J. Kinder

Beacon Hill Press of Kansas City
Kansas City, Missouri

Copyright, 1977
Beacon Hill Press of Kansas City

ISBN: 0-8341-0477-6

Printed in the
United States of America

## *Dedication*

To
the memory of
my mother,
Ibbie Elizabeth Justice,
a cheerful, dedicated,
"kitchen window" missionary

# Contents

# CHAPTER 1

# The Whippoorwill

Even as a bride Mama spiced her conversation with favorite Bible verses, axioms, or pithy sayings handed down by generations of kinfolk. The comfort and inspiration of such helped her and Papa meet the difficulties in starting out on their own. As their problems multiplied in proportion to the family's increase, Mama needed the Bible's wisdom and that of other sources more than ever in rearing her four sons and one daughter.

"God helps those who help themselves," she often proclaimed. Ever a diligent worker, she believed wholeheartedly that the Lord would not fail those who put forth sincere effort.

Once only, while bringing up us children, did Mama fail to quote her favorite belief. That was the year our whippoorwill failed to herald spring out on the chopping block.

"The whippoorwill is late this year," Papa reflected one May night after an arduous day breaking some new ground for seeding.

"He's never been this late before," Mama responded as she sat sewing a shirt for Clayton, their oldest son.

"Whip-poor-will, whip-poor-will," sang John, running to the door.

"My grandfather always said the whippoorwill was a bird of hope and promise." Papa paused to look out the open door. "When the whippoorwill started singing, he knew it was time to plant corn, for spring had truly come to stay."

"So many tales I've heard about the whippoorwill. Uncle Jake once said the whippoorwill was a bird of death." Mama lifted her left eyebrow in thought, a habit she followed when weighing opinions and ideas.

She shivered slightly. "If one sang close to the house, death would come to the family," she added in a low voice.

"Not according to my grandfather," asserted Papa staunchly. "He and Grandma had a whippoorwill all their own, just like ours, right back of the house. Grandma set store by it, the same as she did her pet mare. Always in spring she waited for their whippoorwill."

"Will our whippoorwill sing tonight?" asked John.

"If not tonight, he will come soon," said Papa firmly.

In the special voice that she used for scripture verses Mama quoted softly from Habakkuk: "For the vision is yet for an appointed time, but at the end it shall speak, and not lie: though it tarry, wait for it; because it will surely come, it will not tarry."

In spite of their faith, however, Mama and Papa waited in vain. And after a while, John stopped asking for the bird's song.

In the meantime, Papa and Mama planted the big north hollow in corn. So steep was the terrain that they "dug in" the entire field. Mama, by Papa's side, helped hoe the corn also as she watched the baby, Jettie-Elizabeth, on her pallet in the shade.

Daily the corn grew strong and green. "Never have I seen such beautiful corn," Papa affirmed with pride and thankfulness one summer morning, as he and Mama walked through the rows.

"The green looks lovely with the spidery dew laundering the stalks," answered Mama from her small height of 4 feet and 11 inches.

"The price of our corn and potatoes should see us through the winter," Papa, 6 feet 3 inches, observed confidently as he fingered a sturdy blade.

"Um-um." Mama breathed the fresh morning air gratefully.

She looked up at the shining sun. Its rays shone on her wavy, brown hair and her faded calico dress. She sensed God's presence near, helping the Jennings family in their daily lives.

This day of blue gold sky and sunlight rays was the last bright dawn of hope and promise for my parents that year. Late that afternoon little Jettie-Elizabeth grew desperately ill. She died two days afterward.

A few weeks later a storm lashed down the north hollow and whipped the entire field of corn down to the black soil. The next morning Papa and Mama, with Clayton and John, stood amid an innocent, sparkling sun and watched its fresh beams caress the heavy stalks that now lay lifeless, laden with huge but still immature ears of corn.

For a long, long moment my parents only stood and looked. In the lengthy silence Clayton and John, young as they were, gazed also with tragic adult eyes, as they held tightly to each other's hands. At last the four turned and walked slowly back down the path.

Mama canned and pickled what corn she could. They fed some to the livestock; the rest soured in the field.

Papa and Mama dug 90 bushels of potatoes that fall.

Potatoes were so plentiful, however, that they sold for only 50 cents a bushel. Papa was able to sell only 30 bushels.

"We'll have to make out mighty slim this winter," he said in mid-September.

As always, though, the Lord took care of our family. As he read the Bible aloud each night, Papa enunciated the verses on belief and faith as staunchly as ever. Later, on his knees in prayer, he gripped his huge knuckles together more firmly than before, as he prayed for renewed strength.

Mama, more gentle and quiet, tried to be her natural self for the sake of Papa and the boys. But Papa, ever mindful of her welfare, knew she cried softly to herself at night, missing her baby. He watched her anxiously when she bent her tiny, plump form over the cookstove, or while she sat sewing.

What he noted most was that she did not quote rules and Bible verses like she used to. Yet her faith continued firm, he knew. Not once did her voice falter in helping the boys with their nightly Bible passages.

The next February, Papa, as usual, studied his seed catalogue and spoke of the summer crops.

"But the corn might blow down again," observed Clayton.

Papa's brown eyes studied a picture of sturdy yellow corn. He cleared his throat and noted the sun shining across Mama's soft, wavy hair. Ordinarily she would have had a scripture verse or axiom ready on the tip of her tongue. Now she only bit her sewing thread and remained silent.

At that moment John, playing with a collection of corncobs, turned and by accident knocked down his tunnel.

"Now I'll have to start all over again!" he cried. "Bet

my tunnel this time will be better than ever, though," he added triumphantly.

"Why, that's what you will do when you plant corn again, Papa," declared Clayton in thoughtful wonder. "You will start all over. Maybe there won't be any big storms this year."

Gently Papa laid his hand on Clayton's head. He looked at Mama. Her eyes met his, and for the first time since their baby's death, Mama's smile lighted her whole face as the listless look drained from her sky blue eyes.

"A farmer must always plant again and yet again," Papa told his two sons. "The crops won't always be good but that's a chance one must take. You see, the Lord won't allow those who trust Him to fail all the time. There are bound to be some fair years for everyone."

Papa sowed lettuce the next day. In March he set out onions, planted Irish potatoes, sowed mustard, radishes, carrots, and bedded sweet potatoes. Finishing the potatoes one afternoon, he went down to see old Mr. Simms.

When he returned, he told Mama that Mr. Simms was ailing, and it seemed a pity there wasn't anyone to care for him.

"There's only one thing to do, Will," declared Mama in the old energetic tone Papa hadn't heard in months. "You go right back and bring Dan Simms up here until he gets better!"

"But, Betsey, you shouldn't do extra work just now." A shade of anxiety lay in Papa's voice.

"The Lord will provide," said Mama firmly.

Papa's heart almost turned over inside him. Was she really quoting again?

"I'll go while you prepare supper," he replied joyfully.

In the weeks that followed, Mama waited on Mr. Simms until he grew better. Papa helped all he could, but he was busy himself these days, planting early crops.

While he tilled the soil, March finally made up her mind to depart until another year. April tripped in with the promise of resurrection and new birth. And then time, checking on Deep Valley seasons, left open the threshold for May.

Down by the old mill, Clayton and John picked violets for Mama and waited for the whippoorwill. They waited for something else, too, with happy anticipation. Mama had told them that they might soon have a new baby sister.

On a rain-drenched May morning our brother Jim was born. In the afternoon a golden sun and a colored rainbow appeared together.

That night, at the oncoming of twilight, John was the first to hear the whippoorwill. He had slipped out one last time to listen.

"Oh, Mama, our whippoorwill has come back!" He ran to peek again at his tiny brother. Mama laid a tender hand on his chestnut brown hair. Clayton came and stood beside her, too.

Papa sat reading his Bible near the hearth. He paused to look at Mama and his three sons. He lifted his right hand to his chin in a thoughtful gesture. "It's time to plant the fields," he proclaimed happily after the warm, close moment of togetherness. "We'll have to work hard, boys, but the crops will surely be good this year." He looked directly at Mama, and their eyes locked in rediscovered faith and understanding.

"God helps those who help themselves," asserted Mama in a firm, strong voice. She looked out the open window and watched the fireflies in the purple twilight.

From his wheelchair Mr. Simms looked gratefully at Mama. "God helps those who helps others," he mused.

"All of us work together," said Clayton as he joined

the adult conversation. "So I believe that God helps those who help each other."

Mama's blue eyes threw out rays of warmth for her whole family, including Mr. Simms. She stroked baby Jim's head and quoted softly from the second chapter of Ruth: "The Lord recompense thy work, and a full reward be given thee of the Lord God of Israel, under whose wings thou art come to trust."

"Whip-poor-will, whip-poor-will," proclaimed our whippoorwill at that moment beyond the old chopping block.

"Whip-poor-will, whip-poor-will," echoed John, peeping at the baby again.

"My grandfather always said the whippoorwill was a bird of hope and promise," Papa said softly.

"A bird of hope and promise," Mama agreed.

# CHAPTER 2

# Mama's Rose China Platter

Remembering the whippoorwill, Mama and Papa clung to their renewed faith and the promises of the Bible. They raised future crops and brought other children into the world. Jim was slightly over a year old when brother Jerry was born. A fifth son, William, was named for Papa. He was a bright little fellow, always smiling, and full of energy.

But baby Willie grew ill soon after he learned to toddle under the apple trees, where he delighted in the dandelions and violets. In a few days he died of spinal meningitis. Again Mama and Papa knew heartache. Once more they discerned that the only way to ease pain is to share it with God. They leaned on Him as well when Mama had a difficult time giving birth to me, her last child, and when the meeting house on Pinnacle Mountain was washed away by a flood and we had no place in Deep Valley to attend church. They sensed His presence caring for us when our home burned, and while we lived in the barn until a new dwelling could be built.

When we moved into our new home, the first thing Mama did, after walking over the threshold, was to hang her rose china platter above the mantel in the parlor.

"There," she declared with a satisfied air, "it will help

15

us over the knocks in life here the same as it did in the old house."

Papa, carrying in furniture, momentarily lifted his eyes to the platter. He looked at it fondly but didn't take time to recite the words engraved upon it. Like Mama, he knew them from memory. And he knew also, the same as she, that the courageous lines had helped them climb many a difficult mountain.

Take the time, for example, when Aunt Noreen had lain near death. All night long Mama had watched by her bedside. During the stretched-out weary hours she'd lifted her eyes to the rose china platter, which her great-grandmother brought from Scotland.

"'I can do all things through Christ which strengtheneth me,'" read Mama repeatedly from the Bible verse from Philippians which was lettered on the platter.

"Christ, You can do all things," she prayed softly. Next morning Aunt Noreen was better.

Then there was the time when every crop on our farm failed. Papa and the boys went out looking for odd jobs. At night, in our devotional hour, he read the verse from Mama's china platter.

"It helped us over the rough edges that year," he admitted later.

Now, helping Mama straighten the room, I looked up to observe the platter. It was long, oval, and fragile, with a picture of tiny roses circled around the surface. Inside the circle was the Bible verse. To me it was the loveliest platter in the world.

Absorbed in thought, I scarcely heard the voices on our porch. The neighbors had come from all over Deep Valley for a housewarming. Later, after everyone had left, we discovered a catastrophe had befallen us. Mama's china platter was missing!

In subsequent days we searched everywhere for our

lost possession. "Surely no one would steal my platter," wailed Mama. "Why, that would be like stealing the Bible!"

At length, we were forced to relinquish our search. We had to continue living despite our loss. Other events tumbled about us then, events that unfolded in rapid succession. The winter unrolled into a prolonged white blizzard. Water froze in buckets by the hearth and Miss Effie closed the school for weeks. On an icy day Grandma Simms fell and broke her arm. Two days later Samuel Trelawney died in his sleep after a week of drunkenness. The funeral was held on a snowy day in January.

When spring eventually arrived, though, we almost forgot the cold winter. With renewed hope we planted crops and planned ahead. Somehow that spring, it wasn't the same, making plans without the platter, but we still had the Bible and our faith in God and each other. And as in previous years, our whippoorwill sang near the chopping block.

"And that's enough for the Jennings family or anyone else," asserted Mama as she stood small by the hearth. Yet despite her firm conviction, her blue eyes strayed with longing to the vacant spot above the mantel.

In autumn our harvest was a good one, and we settled down to a second winter in our new home. Mama made several quilts that year. Sometimes she asked Athalena Brown to pass the time of day and help her. Miss Brown now lived alone after her sister's death. She helped folks out from time to time, and they paid her what they could afford.

"Athalena," said Mama one afternoon, "you take these extra quilt pieces home for a quilt of your own."

"Oh, Betsey!" Athalena's eyes shone with anticipation. "You mean I can have these lovely pieces? Why, I've never had anything so pretty!"

17

She coughed, then hesitated a quick second. "Of course, there was the Bible our father left to Jane and me. It burned in the fire—with Jane."

Her voice sank softly, like a faint echo.

"I think I'll go visit Athalena," Mama decided that night after prayers. She tucked a strand of brown hair in the neat bun on her neck. "Growing old all alone must be a weary, lonesome time. I'll take our Bible to read to her."

The friendship between Mama and Athalena ripened fast, like the corn in our cornfield.

"I never saw two women who could find so much to talk about," Papa teased one day.

"And just why shouldn't we share words?" demanded Mama tartly, as she lifted her left eyebrow. "Considering there's so much to contemplate in God's world."

That afternoon, though, Athalena failed to appear for conversation, as she had promised. When Mama went to see about her, she discovered her friend had suffered a stroke. A neighbor helped bring her to our home. Under Mama's care Athalena gradually improved, but she would never be the same again.

"Betsey," said Athalena one rainy winter day, "there's something I must tell you." She coughed and held up her thin fingers in a nervous gesture.

"Wait till you're stronger," advised Mama gently. "Whatever it is, the words will keep."

"No, Betsey, I must tell you now. You see—I have your china platter."

"My platter!"

"Yes—but I didn't steal it!" cried Miss Brown, growing agitated. "That is—not really. Oh, I don't know!"

"Of course not," answered Mama in a brisk manner. "No one with a lovely name like yours could possibly steal my platter."

"But I have it, Betsey. When Sam Trelawney died,

I was the first to reach him. He lay all crumpled up beside the bed—holding the platter in his hands."

Athalena's voice sank to a whisper. "He didn't have a Bible either."

"No Bible!"

"No Bible," replied Athalena. "I guess that verse in the platter meant the Bible to him. Especially at the end, when he knew he'd—soon face God."

Slowly and deliberately Mama straightened the sheet.

"And so I took the platter home," continued Athalena. "I read the verse every night. Oh, Betsey!" The sick woman rose from her pillow. "Go get the platter! And put it back in your parlor. I've repented over and over! Say it wasn't stealing, Betsey!"

"Indeed it wasn't," Mama spoke with calm assurance, "because the platter, you see, has always meant faith and hope to us. No one can steal these necessities or sell them to others. Rather, they're to be shared with friends. And you are my friend," she affirmed positively, as she made the pillow more comfortable.

Mama brought the platter home that afternoon, but she didn't hang it in the parlor. She placed it on the table near the sick woman's bed. Only when Athalena died a few weeks later did Mama return her platter to its rightful place. Hanging it there as a symbol of faith and hope for our family, Mama declared with a satisfied air, "There, it will help us over many a future knock in life. More than ever now, since it's served as a Bible for two people departing this life."

Papa stood pouring more coal on the grate fire. But he took time to stop and read the verse anew.

"'I can do all things through Christ which strengtheneth me,'" he read slowly, savoring comfort from the verse.

19

# CHAPTER 3

# Mama's Kitchen Window

Our new house resembled the old one in many ways. Both were built from sturdy logs which Papa cut from our hillsides. Both contained a parlor; a wide, roomy kitchen with a stove and a fireplace; and a little lean-to off the kitchen. The old house had only two bedrooms, though, whereas our new one had three. Also, we had two little dormer rooms in the attic with bookshelves, a high poster bed, and a discarded sofa. This gave us plenty of sleeping space when relatives and visitors stopped by.

Mama loved her roomy kitchen most of all. That was where we savored the spice of life, she said. A few years after Papa built our new house, he bought a shining glass window for our kitchen. Before that our kitchen had contained a single opening above the worktable, where Mama prepared meals and washed dishes. Covered with screen wire, it provided a glorious view in the spring, summer, and autumn months.

With her hands immersed in dishwater, Mama could let her thoughts soar as she sang the old gospel songs and looked out on the lilacs in bloom, the sunflowers, the velvet marigolds, and the gay sunlight. In the winter months, though, the screen wire was covered by a heavy shutter to keep out the cold. No longer could Mama look out to enjoy the view and delight in the sunlight rays. No longer was she able to see folks coming down the road, crossing the mountain from Lonesome Cove.

"That's why you want your window most of all, Betsey," teased Papa, as he installed the shining pane. "To see folks passing by."

"And why shouldn't I wish to see others of my own kind?" asked Mama rather spicily, arching her left eyebrow. As she lifted her blue eyes then, she laid a gentle hand on his faded flannel shirt. "You enjoy people, too, Will. We both like to invite them in to pass the time of day."

On a shivery November night as Mama looked out her new windowpane, she saw someone carrying a lantern. It was Aunt Sarah Ezelle, who lived over in Lonesome Cove. Her husband, Uncle Joe, had died a while back and she'd had a hard time since. (No, they weren't our aunt and uncle, but we children were taught to address elderly people in this manner.)

Aunt Sarah, in dim twilight dusk, clasped her plaid shawl tightly around her shoulders against the brisk wind.

Mama flung our door wide. "Come in, Sarah," she invited warmly. "It's been ever so long since we've seen you."

"I'm traveling a mite late," said Aunt Sarah, as Mama set a chair by our hearth.

Aunt Sarah laid aside her shawl. She warmed her cold fingers and watched the pumpkin-colored flames leaping up our chimney.

"That wind," said Mama. "I never saw it twirl around so elfishly."

Aunt Sarah sighed. "I washed all day for Mattie

Sloan. Work's getting scarce, though, over in Lonesome Cove, with all the canning stacked on the shelf. Thought I'd travel here in Deep Valley a spell to pick up a coin or two."

Mama set out the leftover dishes from supper. A pleated little frown zigzagged across her forehead. She looked at Papa, who sat mending Jerry's shoe. Their eyes met as they thought of their own financial problems.

The next morning Aunt Sarah watched the sunlight rays stream through our windowpane. "Your kitchen window is so lovely, Betsey. As I hurried down the hill last night, I saw the light shining from it. I knew I'd be safe if I could only reach that light."

Mama looked at the window, bright and glistening. She'd waited so long for the prized possession. At last it had become a reality.

"I'll travel down to Magdalena Lane's after helping you a mite," Aunt Sarah said. "She needs me to help render lard."

"Perhaps you can help me after that. I have meat to can and the soap to make."

Mama stopped to observe the sole leaf clinging to the tree outside the window. "Will and I talked things over last night, Sarah," she reflected slowly. "You've been on the road since Joe's passing. So why not stop with us awhile?"

Aunt Sarah started to interrupt, but Mama paid no heed. "That's what neighbors are for—to help one another in time of need. My Bible tells me that. You'll be helping us, and we'll provide shelter and keep for you."

"I must earn my keep," insisted Aunt Sarah firmly.

"You'll earn it, helping Jenny and me wait on all these menfolk." Mama smiled at me before glancing with pride at Papa and her four sons. "Will," she said then, "I just might set up my cookie and cake store soon. With Sarah's help I could run it now."

22

"Your store!" exclaimed Papa. His tone made us know this topic had certainly not been discussed the night before.

His brown eyes crinkled gaily then. "You've talked of your dream store all these years, Betsey."

"I'll study new recipes and make it pay," affirmed Mama. She held her tiny form straight by Papa's side. "More coffee, Will?" she asked brightly.

"We'll see," said Papa, his eyes serious now. "I may ride into town tomorrow to see Mr. Atwood at the bank."

That was the beginning of the little sweet shop in our backyard. True to her promise, Mama, with her untiring energy, her innate talent for making friends, and Aunt Sarah's help, baked endless stacks of cakes and cookies. The two made money and gradually paid off the bank loan. Thereafter, they carefully kept count of their profits in their little budget book.

Eventually Aunt Sarah saved enough money to plan a little house of her own.

"You're like my family now," she told us. "All the same, though, I need a place of my own."

"A place of your own! But, Sarah—" exclaimed Mama.

"Betsey," Aunt Sarah replied softly, "do you remember that first night I saw your light in the kitchen window? Well, ever since I've wanted a little house with a window just like yours. All shiny glass so I can see folks passing by."

Happily Mama threw a gay look in Papa's direction. "I do so love people, don't you, Sarah?"

"I do now," answered Sarah Ezelle hesitantly. "But not always. Betsey, you taught me to love the neighbors around me—and God."

Her eyes shone with inward happiness. They'd been

23

like that since she accepted the Lord in a meeting at Lonesome Cove two weeks before.

"Why, Sarah—" faltered Mama. For once in her life she had no words ready on her tongue.

"So I want a kitchen window just like yours," Aunt Sarah continued her plans. "And I'll do my best to witness through the window the way you've done all this time."

"Witness through the window?" exclaimed Mama, her voice a note of wonder.

"Indeed you have," asserted Sarah firmly. "Every person you see through that window, you go right out and invite them in to eat victuals. And sooner or later you wind up giving them spiritual food, too."

"Spiritual food?"

"Yes, spiritual victuals, Betsey Jennings. By your interest in people's doings and your showing them what God has done for you."

"Oh, Sarah," said Mama softly.

"Betsey," said Papa, clearing his throat and speaking at last. His brown eyes looked tenderly at Mama. He paused to gaze out her kitchen window where she had lately sowed fresh marigolds.

"Betsey," he began again, shy as always when especially moved, "the boys and I may just add another pane there near the stove."

# CHAPTER 4

# Mama's Sunday Bonnet

Although Mama loved her own kitchen, she felt at home in any kitchen in Deep Valley. She dearly loved to trade recipes with other housewives and try them out in their homes. She exchanged workdays with the other women in quilting and canning. She borrowed from them and they, in turn, borrowed meal, salt, or a spool of thread from her.

"It's one way of getting to know your neighbors," she said. "Being friendly and exchanging things and ideas. It's one way of living the golden rule."

As usual, in the early twilight, Papa sat reading from the Book which contained that rule while Mama sewed in her rocking chair nearby. She sewed diligently, taking tiny stitches in her new bonnet. Her hands moved efficiently back and forth as she trimmed the little circular piece that flowed across the back.

"I've finished the bonnet, Will!" she exclaimed happily, an edge of pride flavoring her voice. "My new Sunday bonnet! I'll wear it to church tomorrow after all."

But Mama was mistaken. She failed to wear her new

25

bonnet to church the next day. Instead, it was worn on someone else's head. For on that particular autumn Sunday Mama lent her bonnet to a neighbor in need even before she wore it herself. Never before had she lent so personal a belonging as her Sunday bonnet!

That morning we'd just finished breakfast when old Ring gave three short barks—his faithful announcement that company had arrived.

"It's Ma," said Janie Bender, her corn-tasseled hair dangling across her eyes. "She's real sick. Can some of you come quick?"

"You do the dishes, boys," Mama directed my brothers. "Come along, Jenny. I'll need your help."

"Will you be back for church?" asked John.

"That depends," Mama answered uncertainly. "If not, you boys run along with Papa. Tell them at church to hold special prayer for Melanie Bender. She needs it."

At Melanie's I saw that Mama was right. "She needs prayer sure enough," I said. "She seems to be awfully sick."

"Stir up the fire," said Mama briskly, raising her left eyebrow as if weighing an opinion. "And set the kettle to boil. We'll need plenty of water to clean up this place."

The kitchen was shivery cold. Janie showed me the woodbox and presently we had a fire leaping in the cookstove. We set the fire burning brightly in the grate as well. Soon the other little Bender girls—Tessie, Sammie, and Joanie—sat huddled close, shyly warming their small fingers.

"Have the children had any breakfast?" Mama asked.

Melanie Bender wearily raised her head. Her brown hair, long and uncombed, flowed about her thin shoulders. Her gray eyes looked desolate and devoid of feeling.

"Nobody's had a bite to eat today." Her voice wilted

like the frost-nipped marigolds. "I just didn't feel like getting up this morning."

Mama's left eyebrow lifted slightly. "Here, let me wash your face," she ordered without further ado. "I feel low myself in the mornings till I've washed up a mite."

Efficiently she reached for a washcloth and a pan of warm water. She washed Melanie's face and began to comb her untidy hair. Janie washed her own face; I tackled the younger girls. Meanwhile, Mama talked of the beautiful fall weather and the fruitful season, trying to cheer Melanie.

"Melanie, I don't believe you're sick at all," she declared emphatically. "That is, in body. It's just that you've let your grief swallow up the best that's in you."

"But, Betsey, I've seen it terribly hard since Sam got killed in that slate fall."

"Of course," said Mama, relenting a bit. "But trouble slides under every door sooner or later." She sighed, thinking perhaps of Jettie-Elizabeth and little Willie.

"Sometimes I think I can't go on!" cried Melanie.

"We all think that," said Mama wisely. "At one time or another."

"I can't, I can't!" screamed Melanie in sudden terror. "I can't go on!"

"Take the girls out to play, Jenny," Mama commanded abruptly. "Come back in 15 minutes."

When I returned to the house, Melanie was still clinging to Mama's hand. Her voice rang out in wild, agitated tones.

"Betsey," she cried, "I burned it, I truly did!"

"Your Sunday bonnet!" exclaimed Mama in disbelief.

"Yes, my Sunday bonnet." Melanie's voice sank to a whisper.

"But why?"

"Why? Can't you see? Because I vowed never to

27

return to church after Sam died. And so—I burned my bonnet."

"Oh, Melanie." A wisp of dew glistened in Mama's blue eyes. "Can't you see that God didn't take Sam to punish you? Death comes to all, child. Whatever the circumstances, all of us harbor guilty feelings, I guess. About the departed, I mean, as we dwell on words said or ones we failed to speak."

"Yes," said Melanie, more rational now. "But I—burned—my bonnet, Betsey. God won't ever forgive me for that because of the reason behind it."

"But of course He will, dear. You have only to ask Him." Mama's voice was soft and comforting, like the fragile, green moss on our hillside.

In a simple, natural manner she knelt by the bed; Melanie and I bowed our heads. And Mama prayed. She prayed earnestly, asking forgiveness for the woman whose heart was burdened with sin. She prayed that the Heavenly Father would strengthen her and give her courage to reach out and take hold of life again, for her own sake and that of her little girls.

"For they're depending on her, Lord," Mama spoke simply and confidently. "So forgive her, dear Father, and help her to depend on You. Cleanse her sick soul and make her know she's forgiven."

When she rose from her knees, Mama placed a firm hand on Melanie's shoulder. "Now you just prop yourself up while Jenny and I cook breakfast."

We prepared a steaming meal for Melanie and the little girls. They ate with relish and were soon feeling much better—all of them. The children ran out to play again while Mama and I washed the dishes.

In the meantime Melanie kept gazing out the window. She watched the sunlight rays chase the frost from our buttery-crimson hills. "Why, it's Sunday," she remembered suddenly. "And I've hindered you two from going to church. Betsey, do you think I can ever go to church again?"

"Indeed you can," replied Mama positively. "You're going to church with us next Sunday."

"But I haven't any bonnet!" cried Melanie, her voice growing nervous and shaky again.

"Melanie Bender," said Mama sternly, "stop that this very minute. You'll have a bonnet to wear to church. I'll see to that."

"But, Betsey—"

"Jenny," said Mama, "run back to the house and bring my Sunday bonnet."

"Your new bonnet, Mama?"

"My new bonnet," said Mama in her decisive voice.

So I ran, knowing that when she used that special tone, she meant business without delay. I soon returned.

"Melanie," she said, "try on my bonnet. You've stayed cooped up in this house so long you've forgotten how it feels to be a lady."

"Oh, Betsey." Melanie took the bonnet gingerly. "It's such a lovely thing."

"Try it on and see how you look," directed Mama, reaching for a mirror. She turned to survey the effect herself. "Now I want to measure just a stitch here—and there—and in the back."

"Oh, Betsey," said Melanie once more.

"I'll make you a bonnet next week. And you'll wear it to church on Sunday!" Again Mama used her decisive tone.

"Betsey, I'm getting out of bed right now," said Melanie Bender with determination. And no one tried to stop her. "There's too much work piled up around this place already. It's not your place to do it for me."

She threw back the covers. While Mama and I looked

on, she knelt quietly on the floor. "There's something I must attend to first," she said simply.

After a long moment she rose from her knees. She reached again for Mama's bonnet. "Betsey, I must learn to do my own praying again. And start standing on my own two feet."

Mama shook the pillows vigorously and started to make the bed. As I helped her, I saw a special gleam in her eyes. And I saw, too, that both her eyebrows were on the same level, the position they occupied when she was in a contented, tranquil state.

"I thank you both for everything," said Melanie gratefully. "And I'll appreciate the bonnet you make. But oh, Betsey, could I wear yours the rest of today, right here in the house? Just to get the feel of a bonnet again—before I enter the Lord's house?"

"Why, of course, Melanie," replied Mama quite matter-of-factly, as if she were lending flour, salt, or a spool of thread. "I'm glad to lend my Sunday bonnet any day."

# CHAPTER 5

# Big Papa's Gold

Mama wasn't the only one in Deep Valley who lent her possessions with a cheerful spirit. Her family, the Greenleafs, were all like that. Although he didn't bear the Greenleaf name, Big Papa's heart reached out to his neighbors, too. Big Papa Tanner was our stepgrandfather.

Our grandmother, who weighed 250 pounds after the birth of her nine children, used her weight and energy to rear her offspring when Grampy Wee died. Grampy had weighed only 120 and had never been able to help Big Mama much on the farm. He died the year that little Willie died.

Big Papa was a huge man. He weighed 275 and was 6 feet 4 inches. Big Mama married him only after she'd started her children to walking their own steps. "And then she had to wait on me!" laughed Big Papa.

Mama loved her stepfather dearly. She said he helped her cross many a stile in life and that his strong faith strengthened hers. She taught us children to depend on his faith and wisdom, too.

Our grandfather loved to commune with God by our

mountain streams. Frequently he and I went fishing to-gether. Sometimes he invited Mike Riley to go with us.

Mike Riley, the only son of old John Riley, lived down at the crossroads where the two forks of Deep Valley trailed together. One day he visited his uncle in town. When he came home, he was the proud owner of a new store-bought pencil box.

On hot afternoons while we played school at Big Papa's behind the smokehouse, Mike gingerly permitted me to touch the shiny pencils and brightly colored crayons. He even let me pull out the tiny compartment inside the pencil box. Big Papa watched us play as he whittled in the shade.

After Mike had gone home, my heart ached with envy. More than anything else in the world, I wanted a store-bought pencil box. But only a few weeks before, another storm had ripped down the old north hollow; and our tall, green corn, just beginning to tassel, soon lay flat on the ground. We would sell no corn that year. Papa was worried about the stock. Mama, stringing fodder beans, wore a puckered little frown above her eyes as she wondered about shoes and clothing.

Although I longed to tell Mama about the pencil box, I said nothing. My thoughts on such a beautiful treasure were only daydreams, of course. Mama had told me about daydreams—pictures you could slide over in your mind, shining ideas you loved to think about even if you couldn't ever quite attain them. Like Tantalus reaching for fruit beyond his grasp, Mama said.

On a dew-drenched August morning Big Papa and I planned to go fishing. I was sitting in the porch swing watching gay splinters of sunlight through the morning-glory vines when he came along with his cornstalk fishing pole and doughball bait. Clayton, my favorite brother, had helped me dig worms, but he wasn't going with us. Instead, he planned to spend the day in our tree house polishing the new play he'd started the week before.

As my grandfather and I started down the road, we spoke only occasionally. Later, sitting on a big rock in the shade of a tall buckeye, he contemplated aloud, "Nothing discovered yet like doughballs to entice a fish. I may help myself to your worms, though, a mite later."

"Help yourself," I replied briefly.

Deep in meditation, I had almost decided to ask Mama about the pencil box. Maybe she could work out something despite the hard times.

"What's pestering you today, Jenny?" Big Papa reached over and patted my shoulder. "You've not spilled 10 words since we started."

I said nothing. Mike Riley had a pencil box, I reflected, and he was only in the fourth grade. I would be in the fifth this year, I reminded myself proudly, tracing pictures in the sand.

Big Papa lowered his pole and stared at the rock cliff across the creek. I sat on my side of the rock, he on his. A pad of silence lay between us.

By lunchtime we had caught several large minnows. Big Papa compared this fishing trip with past ones. Then as he munched the biscuit-jam sandwiches and apples Big Mama had packed for us, he apparently decided the time had ripened to pry me from my shell.

"Nothing like fishing to take one's mind off troubles and ailments," my grandfather pondered leisurely. He crunched his Rome beauty apple. "Just think how our eyes work for us, Jenny, while we sit here. See all the water bubbling past that sprucely washed rock, making a gurgly slush-slushing sound riding over it. Looks pretty, doesn't it? Sounds pretty, too. All crystallike, racing on and on."

I remembered the Bible verse Mama read from

Hebrews about laying weights and sins aside so one could run with patience the race ahead. She said the verse showed us how we should live the lives God gave us.

"Sort of pleasant in this shade among the rocks and flowing water," Big Papa continued his thought. "Leaves still green and dancing in the breeze on old buckeye up there. See the clump of clouds banked against the blue. Lots of pictures creeping in and out. Why, I see a big glacier backing up by the North Pole."

"I see a field of cotton!" I cried. "Two women are picking it. No, one woman and a man."

I don't know who ended up tracing more pictures in the sky that sunlit summer day, Big Papa or the 10-year-old. Our game lasted until our last jam sandwich.

"And then you know," my grandfather said, "a person's ears are valuable. Ever figure out in dollars and cents just how much they're worth? Now what if we couldn't hear cowbells tinkling at lilac dusk? Think what we'd miss if we couldn't listen to old bobwhite's chatter, the humming sound of bees on clover, or to our hens bragging out loud in spring when they feel a sudden inner notion to start laying once more."

"And pipping little biddies when they hatch," I recalled. "And the little calf chasing after Petunia."

"Or Wrangler chasing coons and possums. Or rain dripping on the roof after a long dry spell."

"Or wind whirling around the house in November. Or popcorn hopping up and down in a skillet," I chimed in, biting my juicy apple.

"Or your mama's voice soothing you when you're sick. Or good hymn singing in the meetinghouse." Big Papa reached for his third apple.

"What if we couldn't taste?" he asked. "How thankful I am for the privilege of tasting my food and clear, cold water on a long day of corn hoeing. There's nothing to compare with your grandma's big, fluffy biscuits topped with honey and fresh churned butter, or a groundhog baked just so, all sizzlylike."

My mouth watered as I savored my apple. "Or fried chicken the way Mama fries it. Or peppermint candy that Papa brings from town on Saturdays."

"Yes, a person would really miss a heap of pleasures if he couldn't taste, don't you think?" asked my grandfather.

He changed the position of his pole and brushed a large, black ant from his knotty hand. "Then there's the privilege of being able to smell. What if God hadn't given us that gift? Just think—you'd miss the perfume of apple blossoms and lilacs in spring, the tasty smell of molasses foam in the cane field, and the fresh, green odor of walnuts in the fall."

"And the smell of cakes with red cinnamon berries that Big Mama bakes at Christmas."

"What if you and I couldn't touch things, Jenny?" Big Papa placed his rough hand on a tuft of moss beside the rock. "Feels soft and fringylike—this moss." He lifted fresh black soil and allowed it to sift through his fingers.

"What if we couldn't touch a baby's curling hand or smooth our hands across seasoned prime wood? What if I couldn't rub my old shoulder when it's going to rain?"

"Or feel the shape of a new storybook or the whistles you make for Mike and me? Or a pencil's gliding when you're writing a story?" I asked, as I remembered the unfinished fairy tale I'd hidden above the press door.

Big Papa reached for his pole and my worm can. He breathed deeply with pleasure, enjoying the moment as if another might never unfold. "I've never owned much in worldly goods and never expect to," he decided. "But I, for one, don't waste my time wishing for things not worth even 10 percent of my five senses—the gold that really means something to the human heart."

He stopped to gaze again into the blue above. I finished my second apple and looked, too, visualizing one last picture, a woolly lamb beside a waterfall. The picture reminded me of the story Papa had read about the man who searched for his lost sheep. Ninety-nine of the sheep lay safely in the fold, but the man couldn't rest until he'd found the lost one. If I got lost, my parents and brothers would search the farm until they found me, I knew, because they loved me.

"Yes, sir, gold that really counts—our five senses," Big Papa interrupted my reverie. "Gold given by our Heavenly Father. And meant to be used and appreciated. Else He wouldn't have provided eyes to see, ears to hear, taste buds on the tongue—" Big Papa eyed the two remaining apples.

"Guess we'd better leave those to savor as we saunter home," he decided. "And a smelling sense and hands to touch and feel," he ended happily.

I stuck my hand into the worm can and pulled out a beautiful, long, crawly worm. The sunlight rays peeped through the doily-lace patterns in the trees and made the worm glow brightly in my hand. I smiled and leaned my head against Big Papa's arm before we started fishing again.

Mike Riley could have 10 rich uncles and 50 pencil boxes. At the moment I didn't care. For now I knew I possessed that which was gold indeed. I had five working senses to make me see and hear and taste and smell and feel.

When we went home, I didn't mention the pencil box to Mama. Instead, I told her about the gold our family owned.

# CHAPTER 6

# Mama's Certain Feeling

Mama knew what Big Papa meant when he spoke of the gold that meant something to the human heart. The gold threaded to one's senses, she said, was all tied in with the steps unraveling to your neighbor's door. Mama's steps unraveled to many a neighbor's door, as she used her eyes and ears to see what people needed. Her cousin, Mamie Malone, was also like that.

Whatever Mamie held dear, she invariably shared with others. Like the first ripe strawberries in her wide meadow. She carried them to her next-door neighbors and ate the second mature ones herself. When her cabbages reached maturity, she couldn't enjoy slaw on her own table until Grandma and Grandpa Simms had savored the first head.

When it came to intangible, spiritual values, Mamie acted generously, too. After our old log church on Pinnacle Mountain washed away, she attended meeting over in Lonesome Cove. When she returned to Deep Valley, she shared the spiritual values she'd gleaned with Grandma and Grandpa Simms. Then she'd stop at Lisa

Henson's and tell her, too, about the sermon and God's love.

Lisa was a quiet, wee little woman, wholly unlike Mamie, who stood 5 feet and 11 inches in her wide, comfortable shoes. Lisa avoided crowds. Mamie loved people; she visited someone almost every day.

"I can't figure out why Mamie and Lisa are so close," said Mama one wintry day. "But that is Mamie for you. She doesn't bother with reasons. Her heart is big enough and sufficiently warm to rule her life."

Papa, by the hearth, read from his farm journal.

"Will," Mama said, "did you notice that Lisa went to meeting with Mamie yesterday? The event is only the beginning of something providential. I don't know what that something is, but just watch, because—well, you see, I have a certain feeling about the matter."

Papa looked up suddenly and gazed out the kitchen window. He appeared to size up the sifting, capricious clouds. Actually, he was weighing Mama's declaration about her certain feeling. From past experience, he knew that almost always results unfolded from her positive thoughts.

Lisa continued to attend church with Mamie. Then one Sunday she went forward at the invitation. The whole congregation looked on with breathless anticipation, one question dangling in the uniform silence.

When we got in our buggy to drive home, Clayton voiced the question aloud. "What will Elijah Henson say?" he asked wonderingly.

Everyone knew that Elijah Henson was contrary, dishonest, and the stingiest fellow that ever lived. A huge 235-pound chunk of a man, he glowered from beneath bushy, red eyebrows when he met you in the road. His look made you know he even begrudged the brief, cold "Howdy" with which he acknowledged your presence.

"Something is in the making," Mama decided when no one else commented. She, too, fell silent then as she snuggled close to Papa to keep warm. The boys and I huddled together beneath the pale winter sky.

"Snow is in the making," Jerry said.

The next Wednesday Papa and Clayton returned from the post office, stamping snow from their boots. They brought a new seed catalogue and a dried-apple stack cake that Mamie Malone had sent Mama.

"Mamie says Lisa will be baptized Sunday if the water doesn't freeze over," Papa told us as he thawed out before the leaping firelight. He stared hard at his left shoe.

I edged close to John, who read by the hearth. Jim and Jerry looked up from their fox and geese game. Mama moved to heat coffee for Papa, but she listened intently, the same as all of us. It seemed like an eternity since we'd heard news from the outside world, after the snowfall tucked us in on Sunday night.

"What about Elijah?" Mama asked briefly, as she sliced the cake.

"Oh, Lije is raising the roof, naturally. He says Lisa is not joining any church. All churches want is money from you, he says."

"Guess he's afraid he'll be asked to put in on the new church," Mama said tersely.

I thought of the old barn where the Baptists held services and of the new church they planned to build in the spring. Mama must have visualized the prospect also, because a dreamy look appeared in her blue eyes, the special look that made her see things as they could become with prayer and labor.

"If only someone could get through to Elijah!" Mama lifted her left eyebrow in thought.

"Get through!" Papa stared again at his left shoe.

He had once tried to talk to Elijah about his soul.

39

Exactly how Elijah had treated Papa, none of us knew, not even Mama. I'd heard her tell Big Mama so. "But it's my own private opinion," she'd said, "that Elijah insulted Will unmercifully."

No one except Papa and one preacher had ever attempted to talk to Elijah about spiritual values. Elijah Henson lived as an island to himself, corked up tightly in his huge, grotesque figure. He'd had no dealings with anyone for years, not since he'd quarreled with Dan Bender over a line tree.

On Thursday morning the sun crept forth cautiously at last. When Jim and Jerry wanted to go coasting, I was more than ready.

We skated down to Greenleaf Knoll, the best hill around for coasting. On my third ride I saw old Elijah Henson heading around the bend.

I took one swift glance at the tousled red hair trailing beneath his tall, black hat. His moody, steel blue eyes glinted cold and ferocious under tangled red brows. I grabbed my sled and hid behind a tree. The boys hurriedly joined me.

The road curved in a half circle at the bend. One of Elijah's mules stumbled on a snow-covered rock. For a wavering instant the wagon was suspended between the winding road and the creek.

As the boys and I watched in unuttered surprise, the wagon, mules, and Elijah landed in the frozen creek. At that moment Mamie Malone, tall and erect, marched round the bend, leading her German police dog.

With an appraising glance she observed Elijah and his predicament. She watched the mules break their harness to flee out of sight. She noted Elijah's scattered groceries. Jim and Jerry started toward the creek to help, but Mamie halted them with a wave of her large hand.

"Why, howdy, Elijah," she called to the disconcerted man, who sat in the creek, surrounded by ice chips.

She patted her huge, wolflike dog on the head.

"Pretty cold sitting, uh? Altogether different from your warm fireside last night." She stopped to draw her wool scarf tighter around her neck, then continued relentlessly. "Yes, I went to your house to talk to you about your soul and your selfishness in trying to waver Lisa from considering hers. You shut the door on me. Now you've got to listen!"

A triumphant note echoed in her voice as she patted Hugo again. He waited on his haunches.

"So you mean to stop Lisa from being baptized. You want her to give up her faith even before she begins to savor it. Well, let me tell you, Elijah Henson, she will be baptized Sunday if I have to chain you in the cellar!" Mamie patted the big dog a third time.

The sun scooted behind a doubting cloud. I watched its retreat and shivered against the bare, leafless tree.

After her warning Mamie lashed accusations at Elijah and quoted Bible verses simultaneously. Her talk was as good as any preacher's sermon. It might be the only sermon Elijah's ever heard, I thought, since I'd never seen him in church.

Mamie's interpreting the Scripture to Elijah out in the winter air reminded me of Jesus' talking to the people by the Sea of Galilee. And every time she reached to pat Hugo, loosening his rope a trifle, I recalled the story about Jesus driving the money changers from the Temple.

Briefly the sun slipped out from its hiding crevice, and Mamie ended her talk. Then, just like a preacher, she commanded, "Now let us pray."

She knelt beside the snowy road. Before the boys and I bowed our heads, I looked at Elijah, shivering in the

41

creek. He reached up slowly to remove his old, black hat and then bowed his huge, shaggy head.

Unlike Mamie's sermon, her prayer was brief. She prayed only that God's will be done through His weak human instruments.

Mamie rose from her knees. She beckoned to the boys and me. She reached her large, efficient hands to Elijah and led him from the icy creek.

The next Sunday practically everyone in our valley attended church in the barn over in Lonesome Cove. Around the old Ben Franklin stove, we heard preaching such as we'd never heard before. On Papa's knee, because of the crowd, I listened to every word, since that was the type of sermon we heard that day—the kind you couldn't help but listen to attentively. It was all about God's love for mankind, forgiveness, and the honest searching and sifting of our hearts.

At the end of the sermon all eyes turned to the back of the barn. For on the creaking floor planks Elijah Henson heaved himself from his seat and walked laboriously to the front. When he passed by, I searched his face to see if he looked the same or if he'd really been "born again" as the Bible said.

He must have been, I decided, for tears trickled from his pale blue eyes—eyes that were no longer frozen and forbidding. Instead, they were now warm and sad and joyful, all at the same time. God had changed this man and he would walk a different path because of his rebirth.

At the creek, people relived the history of former baptizings. "I never knew anyone to catch cold over being baptized, no matter how low the temperature," asserted Thomas Sands.

Back by our warm hearth, we talked of Lisa and Elijah Henson making Deep Valley news when they were baptized together while the temperature hovered around zero.

"Mamie Malone had a hand in it all," declared Jim. "She really dished out the Bible verses to Elijah that day."

"Mamie never keeps things for herself alone," commented Clayton.

"Least of all her religion," reflected Papa, as he lifted his right hand to his chin in a thoughtful gesture.

"Only by sharing our faith with others can we keep it growing for ourselves," Mama spoke contentedly.

I leaned against her arm and thought of old Elijah and how his eyes had changed when he ambled up to give the preacher his hand.

Mama looked out the shining pane of her store-bought window. "Now all along I had this certain feeling," she began, as she looked at Papa, who sat watching the orange red firelight glow.

# CHAPTER 7

# Big Mama's Thanksgiving Plate

On Thanksgiving morning the sun stretched out pale rays and then scooted on over into Deep Valley. Mama and I loaded up the dried apple and pumpkin pies, the stack cakes, and the iron kettle of shuck beans. Clayton and John drove old Blarney around to the kitchen door. Jim and Jerry carried out the food. Papa checked the fires, and we were ready to drive to Big Mama's for Thanksgiving dinner.

At my grandmother's we warmed our cold fingers in the kitchen. All kinds of appetizing food steamed away on the huge cookstove—juicy, red sweet potatoes simmering in brown sugar and a mite of molasses, hot white potatoes, and yellow corn Big Mama had canned in the summer. In the oven the turkey and dressing roasted slowly.

"You make the cornbread, Betsey," my grandmother directed. "I'll do the biscuits."

"We'll heap up the woodbox." Clayton spoke for himself and the younger boys.

"Will, let's saunter to the barn," said Big Papa. "The new colt came last night."

I set one side of the table and then waited, knowing that Big Mama allowed no one but herself to arrange the other side. She reached for the blue willow plates and placed three. Close beside her own plate at the end she placed another—Big Mama's empty plate, we called it.

Setting the plate, Big Mama declared, as always, "Never can tell. Some stranger passing by might come hungry."

She'd set the plate over three years now—ever since Uncle Seth went away. He wrote only twice after he left, and Big Mama had often lain awake at night, sifting anxious thoughts. She wondered if he might be cold or sick or hungry. When she first set the plate, she set it for Uncle Seth, hoping for his return. Later, though, even after news came that he probably drowned in the Elkins Bridge disaster, she continued to set the empty plate.

"Never can tell," she repeated, as usual. "Some stranger passing by might come hungry." If her boy no longer needed food, some other mother's son might stop by in need of it—and occupy Seth's place.

Big Mama spoke of her son now. "Betsey, he's not coming back. Yet I keep hoping despite everything."

"It's best to accept the fact, I suppose," Mama spoke thoughtfully. "Seth would surely have written by now if he were still alive."

"I know, but he did go three months there at first without writing." The pain of neglect lingered in Big Mama's eyes, even after all this time.

"Mama, you know men. They never relish writing letters. Even Seth would have written by now, though." Mama stirred the cornmeal vigorously.

My grandmother opened the oven to peek at the turkey. "Betsey, he went right—you think, trusting the Lord?"

"Mama! You know he did!"

45

Big Mama's eyes held a tiny glint of doubt.

"Now, if you're still thinking of the time when Seth ran around with that wild crowd who ended up in the pen, just slide the notion from your head. He quit their company after he saw them turning the wrong corner."

Mama placed a comforting arm around her mother. "Seth could never forget your teaching. No matter where he traveled, he surely remembered God's Word. You read too much for him to forget it for long."

"Why, of course," said Big Mama brusquely, as she pushed a gray white curl into the bun at her neck. "Why should I talk so on such a day of blessings?"

At the table we bowed our heads while Big Papa listed our blessings, flavored with his unique manner of expression. When I lifted my head, I stared at the empty plate. Would it ever be filled with hot, steaming food?

Mama was passing the beans to Papa now, and Big Papa carved expertly on the turkey. "A drumstick, Jerry boy?" he asked. A knock sounded on the door and he held the knife in midair.

My grandmother rose hurriedly. She opened the door and the cold air rushed in. A drummer boy with his pack of peddling notions stood hesitantly on the porch. His sleeve was torn and blood oozed from a cut in his wrist.

"I fell at the end of the bridge," the boy said. "May I come in?"

"Here, boy." Big Mama pulled my grandfather's rocking chair close to the hearth. "Toast yourself by the grate."

Mama reached for the teakettle. She prepared a pan of water and gently washed the boy's wrist.

"The roads in these parts are rather winding," he commented. "I'm not used to the mountains. I left the level land a month ago."

"The level land?" A questing look of hope leaped in

46

Big Mama's blue eyes. "Did you ever run across a Seth Greenleaf?" she asked slowly, her voice trailing at the end.

The boy shook his head. The tiny glimmer of hope faded from Big Mama's eyes. Resolutely she held her shoulders high and started toward the attic stairs. At the first step she paused briefly, as if to turn back, then went ahead in new determination.

When she returned, she brought a faded plaid shirt that had belonged to Uncle Seth. She reached it to the boy and hung his wet shirt to dry.

"Here, boy," she said, leading him to the empty plate. She heaped the plate high with food.

"My parents died when I was 12," the drummer boy said. "I've had to shift for myself since." I liked the sound of his voice. It was honest and sturdy like Papa's voice.

"No kin?" asked Big Mama.

"None close." The boy cut his turkey. "Say, this is the best food." He smiled in appreciation. "You people are sure good to take me in like this."

Big Papa started to carve again. "More turkey, boy?"

"My parents were a lot like you," the boy confided. "Friendly to strangers, like the Good Samaritan. They took me to church and read the Bible to me."

I looked at Big Mama, remembering how she'd read scripture to Uncle Seth. Her eyes shone with sudden radiance, filled with love and renewed faith.

"Seth went right, trusting in the Lord," she asserted clearly. With positive faith ringing in her voice, she looked straight at Mama.

"Why, of course he did," Mama agreed. "He couldn't ever forget what you and Big Papa taught him."

"This is the best Thanksgiving we've had in years!" my grandfather proclaimed in his booming voice.

"The best Thanksgiving," agreed my grandmother softly.

From that time on young Tim Evans ate from Big Mama's empty plate. He gave up peddling and remained on the farm to help my grandparents. With a plate heaped high with food, you can't continue calling it an empty one. So we began calling it Tim's plate.

My grandmother, though, always thinking of others, just had to set another plate. It was Tim who named this one "Big Mama's Thanksgiving plate" in memory of the day when he became part of a family again.

It reminded him, too, of his mother, he said, and of a favorite Bible verse she had read to him: "For I was an hungered, and ye gave me meat: I was thirsty, and ye gave me drink: I was a stranger, and ye took me in."

Big Mama liked and read that verse from the 25th chapter of Matthew, too. She remembered it when she set the plate, not only on Thanksgiving Day, but on every day of the year.

After that special Thanksgiving Mama set an empty plate at our house, too. "Never can tell," she declared, as she looked out the window down the road. "Some stranger passing by might come hungry."

CHAPTER **8**

# Mama's Breakfast Special

Mama's oatmeal was a special anytime she prepared it. First, she started it bubbling in an old black kettle. She then added a swish of salt, sprinkled it lightly with a trail of brown sugar, and set it to simmer on the back of the stove.

By the time she cooked the rest of breakfast, the oatmeal was savory and ready. We ate it first while the big platters of eggs and meat, the biscuits and gravy remained hot on the stove.

On a rain-drenched morning in early May, however, Mama was so busy talking that she forgot the platters. The rest of us became so involved then in the conversation that we also forgot we were hungry. By that time other events developed, so we ate nothing but oatmeal that morning.

From that time on Papa called the oatmeal Mama's "breakfast special." He said the oatmeal she prepared tasted so satisfying that it was a complete breakfast without her other special foods.

That morning we were eating away, all seven of us,

while the rain continued to pour from the sky. Papa kept eyeing the garden. Mama, for some reason, kept her eyes cast down and her mouth snapped tightly shut like the lids she'd screwed on her mustard greens the week before.

"Will," she spoke eventually, "what did you think of Pastor Horne's sermon Sunday?"

Pastor Horne was the young pastor of the little white Presbyterian church built down near the mouth of Deep Valley. We attended church there now instead of going to Lonesome Cove.

"The sermon?" echoed Papa vaguely, as if his thoughts were elsewhere.

"Well, didn't you think he seemed a bit stirred up, so to speak?"

"Perhaps."

"He just as good as said that some of us are hypocrites," decided Clayton.

"I wonder—" began John in the serious tone that was a natural part of him.

The rest of us sat expectantly, waiting to share John's wonderment. But typical of my second brother, he didn't enlighten us.

"Pastor Horne seems to think we aren't giving our religious principles sufficient exercise," continued Mama. "He says the muscles of our faith aren't developing."

"In other words, we need to start walking the second mile," Clayton summed up the situation.

"Exactly," Mama commended him. "We stay too wrapped up in our own families and work. That must be what he meant."

"Labor is necessary," Papa replied slowly, as he looked out the window. He'd planned to plow the west 40 that day.

"We help each other, of course." Mama evidently itched to pursue the topic despite Papa's reticence. "And our relatives naturally. At least the nearest ones," she added honestly.

"When it isn't too much trouble?" asked Clayton lightly.

"But they help us in return," decided Jim.

"Uncle Bartley helped us build the barn," Jerry remembered.

"And the new fence," I added.

"Is that really helping, though, when one is repaid?" asked John thoughtfully, emerging from his reverie.

Outside the rain spattered harder than ever. Silently we attended to our oatmeal bowls.

"Deep Valley is such a little place," reflected Mama after a brief silence. "There's opportunity for service among ourselves, of course. And I believe that we can serve God even in the everyday matters of life."

"But that isn't exactly traveling the second mile for others?" probed Clayton, almost cheerfully.

Mama looked intently at her oldest son. Was he teasing her again? He did sometimes when she grew too serious. But Mama—and the rest of us, too—loved Clayton's gaiety. It made life spicy for us, not knowing what to expect next from him.

Most surely, we didn't expect the knock on our door— not at that hour and in the deluge outside. But the hurried knock was decidedly there, a concrete reality in contrast to the abstracts we'd been discussing.

Mama rose quickly to answer. On the wet threshold stood a man in shabby overalls and an old raincoat. A limp, black hat covered straggly salt-and-pepper hair that crept out in zigzag fashion from the brim.

The man's eyes held desperate glints. "Could you all come and help?" he cried brokenly. "We've lost the littlest ones. And Nannie—"

"Come inside," Mama commanded in the precise tone she used with all of us. "And tell us about your troubles."

His name was Lem Ezelle, and he was a distant cousin to Aunt Sarah's husband. He'd moved to Deep Valley the previous week. When his wife had taken sick around four o'clock that morning, he'd gone for the doctor. Back home he found the children missing. Nannie seemed better now, but she was frantic about the three-year-old twins.

"Pastor Horne was right," Mama commented in a low tone as if talking to herself, while she hastened to gather food. "To think that they've lived here a week and we didn't take the trouble to find out. Strangers among us and in need of help."

By this time the boys had gone to the barn and hitched up our buggy. Papa and Mr. Ezelle carried the baskets of food. Mama and I followed with the platters from the stove.

Our destination, we found, was Licking Branch on the left fork of our valley. The Ezelles lived in a discarded chicken house! When we entered the door, I glanced briefly at Mama. She said nothing but I knew her thought. Once more she was reviewing Pastor Horne's sermon and the fact that strangers had moved among us without our making it our business to help them in their need.

Strangers—but Mrs. Ezelle didn't seem like a stranger. She was a tiny, girlish woman. Her sad, gray blue eyes reminded me of a lonely, desolated rock cliff. As she drank the tea Mama made, she attempted to smile gratefully.

Mama soon had a hot fire in the cookstove. I dressed the three children who sat on a pallet near the fire: a little boy about four, and two little girls, perhaps seven and nine years old.

Outside Papa, Mr. Ezelle, and the boys searched for the twins. They found them in a cave near the woodland, sleeping beside their dog. Papa came in carrying the little girl and boy in his arms. Again I saw that look in Mama's eyes, the special look that made me know her thought.

Quietly and efficiently Mama reheated the food she'd prepared at home. She stirred the oatmeal she'd brought along to cook at the Ezelles'. She took a plate to Mrs. Ezelle and motioned the others to the table.

And so we watched the family eat the remainder of our breakfast. It seemed we'd eaten our oatmeal a very long time ago. Since then a lot had happened—events which made us aware that practicing one's Christian faith can truly be a satisfying actuality—events that gave us an opportunity to walk the second mile for others. Was this what our pastor had in mind?

"Lem," said Papa, as he reached for his hat, "I'll need help when this spell breaks. Can you come up and help me a few days?"

The look in Mr. Ezelle's eyes showed that a man with a growing family would be glad to work.

"Nannie," said Mama, tying her bonnet strings, "I'll be back tomorrow. When you get well, you and the children must visit us. I have a bag of extra quilt pieces if you'd like to sew them." A woman with five children can always use extra quilts, and she was grateful.

And so we left them there—in the chicken house slowly being made into a home. We left them to return to our own comfortable farmhouse where, once more, we sat down to eat another kettle of Mama's "breakfast special," her savory oatmeal.

But we would go back to see the Ezelles again—because that was just the beginning, if we, as a family, working together, truly meant to live and walk the second mile.

# CHAPTER 9

# Mama's Wedding Ring

When Mama stood at the altar, she'd had us in mind, she said. She used to dream about the children she and Papa would have around their table and the home we'd share together. When she said this, she looked down at her wedding ring.

Mama's wedding ring was a plain gold band that she'd worn since her wedding day. Not once had she removed it from its secure position. Her ring was a symbol of the sacred contract she'd signed to walk by Papa's side for life.

On a spring afternoon Mama walked happily by his side as they entered the church door. They sat close to share the meaningful moments while Pastor Horne united Mike Riley's oldest sister and Tim Evans in marriage.

On the way home, Mama looked up at the April sky. "It was a beautiful wedding," she declared.

"It is good to see two young people start walking together," Papa replied.

"Despite the unraveling of problems?" asked Mama, impishly smiling up at him.

Papa smiled his own rare smile as he remembered a problem or two, or maybe more, which they had unraveled together. "Yes, despite everything," he affirmed.

Tim Evans, the drummer boy who had lived at Big Mama's after eating Thanksgiving dinner, stood tall by his new bride that spring and summer. But as the summer days wilted and the first autumn chill crept over our hills, the love between the couple cooled through everyday routine. Late one Saturday evening Anna Lou Evans knocked timidly at our door.

"Betsey," she began, lifting her grief-filled eyes, "Tim and I had a fight."

"Indeed." Mama lifted her left eyebrow as she sized up the announcement.

She looked up. The autumn sky was sagging like an old black tarpaulin. "The rain will set in for keeps directly. Come on in," she invited, warming her tones to agree with her words.

She led Anna Lou to the hearth, then sat in her rocking chair mending Papa's sock.

"Betsey, this isn't the first time Tim and I have disagreed," Anna Lou confided in a low voice.

"And it won't be the last," Mama spoke practically as she examined the hole in Papa's sock.

Anna Lou started crying. "I thought everything would be just perfect," she said brokenly. "And now my marriage has to end like this."

"End!" echoed Mama, blending her stitches together. "Nonsense, child. Why, this is only the start of your marriage. Everyone stumbles in reaching a goal. I guess it's necessary for us to fall at times so we can straighten up to look toward the sky again."

Anna Lou stared mournfully at the darkening sky. "What can I do? I can't go home. Papa would throw a

55

fit! He was against my marrying so young in the first place and told me not to run back if things went wrong.''

She twisted her hands nervously and looked down at the left one. "And I can't ever go back to Tim again because—oh, Betsey—I threw away my wedding ring!''

When she heard this, Mama dropped her thread. "Anna Lou Evans, how could you possibly have done a thing like that?'' she demanded.

"But, Betsey, I couldn't wear it after Tim said all those mean things.''

Mama laid her mending aside. "You can't return home in this rain. But in the morning—''

"I'm never going back to Tim!'' Anna Lou cried convulsively.

The next morning, though, the young bride announced rather shamefacedly that she would return home. "After all, I did nag Tim about dawdling around in town,'' she admitted. "He didn't argue back for a long time since he is good-natured, you know.''

"Um.'' Mama lifted her left eyebrow. "What about your ring? You can't let Tim know you threw it away.''

"I'll find it. I threw it in the lilac bush.''

Anna Lou wore her ring five days before she returned for a second visit. Once more she and Tim had quarreled over trivial matters. This time she'd thrown her ring in the quilt scraps. As the weeks passed, the ring lay tossed beneath the front porch, under the apple tree, or behind the bed while the young wife continued to call on Mama.

One afternoon in late October she knocked at our door. "Betsey,'' she said, "I envy you never having to throw away your wedding ring.''

"Indeed.'' Mama lifted her eyebrow higher than usual.

"Yes. It's different with you, though, since you and Will never disagree.''

Mama looked directly at Mrs. Evans. "No marriage partners can say that they never disagree. If they do, they're either lying or have become angels," she spoke straightforwardly.

"But, Betsey, you and Will get along beautifully."

Mama's eyes twinkled. "We don't always view matters in the same light," she confessed.

Her voice changed to a serious note. "When we have differences, we pray about them, dear," she witnessed to the younger woman. "We ask the Lord to guide our feet of clay."

"Oh." Anna Lou sat quietly. "Tim and I have neglected church attendance," she admitted in a low tone.

After supper Papa tackled a job he always dreaded. And Mama didn't relish the prospect either, since he could never put up new stovepipes without growing angry. In anxiety she'd begged him to wait until after Anna Lou was gone. But this was one year, Papa assured her, when he wouldn't permit his temper to get the best of him over the difficulty of fitting stovepipes.

In a determined manner he began the task. With laborious effort he fitted the first two joints. He stopped to survey his success with pride. He started on the third joint with deep concentration. But alas, despite all intense effort, it refused to notch correctly and all three joints crashed to the floor! Soot poured from the chimney and showered Papa's frustrated face with the thick, black dust.

"Betsey," he stormed, "of all the outlandish, cantankerous jobs, this reaches the limit! Now where did you put the shears? Can't you ever leave my tools alone?" he demanded belligerently.

"Will Jennings, I didn't have your shears!" retorted Mama, unwilling to shoulder unmerited blame.

One sentence led to another with increasing tension

between the two. Even after the pipes were at length installed, my parents remained aloof from each other.

By Sunday morning, however, prayer and meditation had restored them to a more cheerful spirit. They got ready for church while Anna Lou prepared to return home.

"Betsey," she said, as she watched Mama straighten Papa's tie, "you never once considered throwing your ring away when you and Will grew angry last night, did you?"

Mama looked down at her gold band. She smiled at Papa. "Why, of course not. Will placed it there on our wedding day. And I've never taken it off since."

"I'm going home to find my wedding ring!" Anna Lou spoke determinedly. "And I'll never throw it away again!"

She looked down at her left hand. "Betsey," she said quietly, "I prayed about my marriage in your guest room last night."

Mama placed a gentle hand on her shoulder. "You've grown up at last, dear."

In church that day Mama and Papa sat closer than usual. In the next pew young Mr. and Mrs. Timothy Evans also sat close in the holy place. All four seemed bound together in a spirit of unity.

Mama smiled suddenly and looked down at her wedding ring.

# CHAPTER 10

# Mama's Youngest Brother

The morning sun drew back the thick curtain of fog. Mama and Mamie Malone stood under a large oak tree, preparing a fresh pan of batter. Nearby, the other women fried pancakes over the red coals. The buttery fragrance drifted across the chilly October air.

"We'll never get them out now," declared John Sands.

His voice, resigned and hopeless, dropped to a low tone.

Uncle Seth, Mama's youngest brother, had come home at last, alive and well—alive, that is, until a slate fall in the mine had engulfed him and his companions. Practically everyone was now working to get Uncle Seth, Ben Simms, and Thomas Sands out of that black hole in the side of the hill.

The men had taken turns going into the mine. The women held prayer sessions and kept coffee and food ready. The boys kept the fires going, and the girls and I washed dishes.

My hands were immersed in suds as I noted the sun's rays on the crimson-tipped leaves. Would my uncle and the other men ever see the sunlight again? I shut my eyes, then opened them quickly, thankful that I could see the beauty around me.

Uncle Seth loved the sunlight, too. He liked tramping in the woods on sunlit autumn days. Only the week before he had taken my brothers and me to Pinnacle Mountain to gather nuts. On the trip he'd told us about his loneliness in tramping the city streets after leaving home.

He didn't tell us about his card playing and gambling his money away, but we'd heard Big Mama tell Mama that. Our grandmother had also told Mama about the fight Uncle Seth had in a saloon and how he received the blow which knocked him into amnesia. During that period Salvation Army workers discovered him, and when he recovered, they persuaded him to return home.

Big Mama couldn't find sufficient words of praise for the Salvation Army folks. They not only returned her son home to eat from his empty plate, but they'd led him to his knees, seeking God's mercy.

After Uncle Seth's conversion, a change had occurred in him as he sought to practice Christ's teachings.

"He's so different from what he used to be," Mama asserted.

Papa had nodded assent.

"For one thing, my brother is more humble and compassionate. Of course he was always kind and gentle, despite his bad habits."

Again Papa nodded agreement.

"Seth is letting his religion prey too much on his mind, though," Mama had reflected then. "He can't feel called to preach, most surely. He's never made use of what words he knows."

Papa had smiled with a twinkle in each eye. He knew that Mama invariably made use of all words at her command. To her, words were like love. The more you gave away, the more they multiplied when you needed them.

"Your brother senses his new faith deeply." Papa had measured his thought carefully. "So much so that he

Sue and Eric ran quickly to the tree where the bluebird was chirping so excitedly. There was a big hole in the side of the tree. Sue poked her head in quickly and there was Towser standing on his hind legs inside the hollow tree. He was vainly trying to get out.

Eric quickly untangled Towser's leash and lifted him gently out of the tree. Towser was so happy to see Sue that he danced on his hind legs as he ran to greet her. Sue, Towser and Eric then ran across the fields for home.

would set forth like the prophets of old if he possibly could."

Mama agreed. "Only the other day I came upon him reading Jeremiah. But Seth will never be a Jeremiah or an Isaiah. He's too sparing of words."

Now, taking more plates to Mamie Malone, I recalled that Uncle Seth had also read the story of Jonah. Uncle Seth and the others had been inside the mine three days and nights now. Like Jonah, in the darkness they must have had plenty of time to think.

"More plates, girls," called Mamie then.

"No, we'll never get them out now," said John Sands again.

"Betsey!" called Papa from the mine. The trapped men had been found!

Mama stood protectively by her youngest brother as he sat shivering by the fire. Tenderly she laid her hand on his damp shoulder.

Ben Simms spoke up. "I've attended meeting for years," he confided to the group, "but no words ever reached me like Seth's explanation there in the mine. He explained the pathway of salvation in such simple, everyday words that I understood at last."

Thomas Sands remained silent, meditating. He too had heard Uncle Seth's words in the mine. They must have meant something to him during those agonizing hours.

In the crowd Uncle Seth was again shy and reticent. At our supper table that night, though, he once more spoke for his Lord. "I really had time to think in the mine," he reflected.

He held his fork in the air and stopped so long I thought he would never go on. Mama piled more ham on his plate. Papa passed the beans to Jim, and Jerry asked for the potatoes. It would soon be time for our apple pie if Uncle Seth didn't hurry his words along!

"There in the dark I thought of all the prophets whom God called for His purposes," my uncle spoke at last. "I thought especially of Jonah."

Again Uncle Seth stared long at his plate. He stared so hard at the blue china that Mama could wait no longer. "We can't all be Jonahs or Jeremiahs," she declared emphatically. "Or all the leaves on the tree."

Uncle Seth slowly lifted his eyes to hers. "That's what I finally understood—that I'm only plain Seth Greenleaf."

Mama couldn't wait to answer.

"But you're the only Seth Greenleaf in all of Deep Valley," she hurried to say, "and very important because of that particular role." She stopped to look fondly at her brother. "Who else can play it?" she demanded.

Encouraged by her comment, Uncle Seth continued, "I found that I could talk to Ben and Thomas. I told them about God. I think—I helped them."

"Of course you did," asserted Mama staunchly. "And you'll be helping others, too."

"But only one or two at a time. I don't have words for more than that."

Rising to her feet, Mama agreed heartily. "Each to his own," she commented placidly. "There are plenty of ones and twos in the valley needing to hear God's Word." She reached for the apple pie and began to cut it.

"No, we can't be all the leaves on the tree. We can be only the special leaf on our own particular branch. But each single leaf is necessary and helps the tree to grow strong and reach toward the sky."

Uncle Seth smiled a slow smile of appreciation.

I was proud of my youngest uncle—the only Seth Greenleaf in Deep Valley. He would now go out and tell the "ones and twos" about God, because Mama had helped him discern the worth of individual witnessing.

# CHAPTER 11

# Mama's Only Sheet

As the months passed, Mama helped shy Uncle Seth in his missionary efforts. If she heard of someone whom she thought he could reach, she never stopped until she arranged a meeting for the two.

"I once meant to be a missionary myself," she reflected once as she looked out the window, while my brothers and I reviewed our Sunday school verses for her.

A wistful note crept into her voice. I wondered what lay back of the dream that had failed to reach fruition. But after the incident of the two drummer boys, Mama's dream no longer seemed to be unfulfilled.

Mama must have felt the same way. Never again did she sigh over the fact that she had missed the opportunity of becoming a missionary. As always, she continued living out the message of God's love daily as she played the role of our mother, Papa's wife, and a Christian neighbor.

One role Mama played to perfection. She could iron clothes so smoothly that they looked almost brand-new. "I'll iron the sheet today," she said one sunlit morning, as she tested her black iron on the stove. We had but one sheet for the family and took turns using it.

"It goes on your bed today, doesn't it, Mama?" I asked, folding the towels. She nodded and started to smooth the wrinkles.

The hard times in our valley had been difficult for everyone. We'd had two lean harvests in succession and hadn't bought any extras for a long time. Our clothes were wearing out and now we were down to our last sheet, despite Mama's skill in mending. That is why we took turns sharing it—all seven of us. One week Clayton and John enjoyed its smooth whiteness on their bed. The following week Jim and Jerry shared it together. My turn came next. And then Mama and Papa owned the sheet for a whole week. Each of us longed for the arrival of our turn.

"How much money do we have now?" I asked Mama.

She glanced toward the baking powder can where we kept the egg money. "One dollar and 80 cents. With muslin 10 cents a yard, we'll soon have enough for four new sheets."

"Oh, Mama, then we'll have a new sheet for all the beds!"

She rested a minute and looked out the window to gaze at the violets edging about the barn and the yellow dandelions on the lawn. "Someone's coming up the road," she announced.

I looked, too. A drummer boy with his pack of notions rounded the bend of the road. As Mama and I watched, another boy exactly like the first followed him.

They entered the yard. I ran to call Papa and the boys from the field. The twin brothers displayed their merchandise while each of us examined it with care.

"I'm afraid we can't buy anything today," Papa spoke regretfully. He noted the worn clothes of the two sandy-haired boys and knew they were in need. "We've had a streak of hard luck lately. Just now, we want to finish planting our corn before the rain begins."

"We can help," one twin told Papa eagerly.

"For a night's lodging, that is," the other added quickly. "We have to sleep on the road if we don't get a place."

That night the twin brothers slept in my bed while I slept on the floor near Mama and Papa. As she prepared my bed for the twins, Mama unfolded our only sheet. Generously she gave her best to the strangers.

"They're so young to be traveling on their own," she remarked as she smoothed the sheet. "I wonder if they have a mother to do for them."

That night we heard about the homelife of the boys. "Father died when we were 10," Paul told us. "So we've made the living since. Mother broke her hip and stayed in a wheelchair a long time."

Mama turned to look at her four sons. She looked up at Papa. "Here's the Book, Will," she said gently, as she reached our big red Bible toward him. "Read a comforting passage tonight."

Papa read from the Psalms in his measured tones. As he read, our guests stared at the Bible. They acted as though they'd never heard the Scriptures before!

At breakfast the next morning James told Mama that it had been ages since he'd enjoyed such a good night's sleep. "It was nice sleeping on a smooth sheet," he confided.

He hesitated as if to say more. "Just nice, that's all," he finished briefly, looking at his brother, who remained silent.

I looked at Mama as her eyes met mine. We were thinking the identical thought. More than likely the boys had never before slept on a smooth sheet!

There was only one thing to do after that, of course.

Mama, always ready for impromptu emergencies, acted without further ado. With a firm, swift step she started toward my room. She returned presently with her only sheet.

"Here, boys," she said, addressing the twins as she might have spoken to my brothers. "Take this sheet. You may need it on the road."

"Why, Mrs. Jennings!" exclaimed Paul.

"Thank you," said the pair.

"Here's something else, too." Mama's voice was soft as she handed two fragments of paper to the boys, papers that contained the priceless words of the 23rd and the 46th psalms.

"I copied these verses for you last night," she said quietly. "You'll need them on the road also. They can help you over the rough spots each day."

By this time she was standing near the table where our Bible lay. Gently she laid her hand on its worn cover. "This Book, you see, has helped our family weather many a storm," Mama witnessed to the drummer boys.

Again the two stared at the Bible in much the same manner that they'd gazed at it the previous night.

"We never had one in our house," said Paul in a low tone.

"No Bible!" I uttered without thinking.

Mama's left eyebrow lifted above me and her eyes, like lightning darts, alighted sternly on me.

"I'm sorry," I said.

"We've only one Bible," said Mama, her hand still on the Book, "else I'd give it to you. But you boys read the words on those papers. They'll help you along."

"We'll buy us a Bible!" affirmed Paul in sudden inspiration.

"Yes, that's what we'll do. We'll buy us a Bible," agreed James.

The boys waved good-bye from the gate. "Thank you again, Mrs. Jennings, for the sheet. And for this, too," called Paul as he held up the portion of the Book which Mama had made for him. "We'll buy us a brand-new Bible!" he proclaimed again, as he latched the gate.

Mama, Papa, my four brothers, and I silently watched the pair until they disappeared around the bend.

"Your only sheet," said Papa, as we returned to the kitchen. "That was your only sheet, Betsey."

From her small stature Mama looked up at Papa's stalwart form. Then her eyes turned toward the violets near the barn and the dandelions trimming our lawn. "We'll buy more sheets, dear," she affirmed cheerfully.

"Those boys will go far," she predicted then in the same positive tone. "With the Lord by their side they can't do otherwise."

"Betsey," said Papa, "you never fail to tell others about the Lord."

Mama smiled as she looked out her kitchen window. "Set two empty plates at the table from now on, Jenny," she directed softly. "Never can tell how many strangers may enter our valley from the outside world."

# CHAPTER 12

# Mama and the Missionary Barrel

The passing of drummer boys and others flavored the days with an extra dessert. The arrival of our missionary barrel was always a special treat also. Each year we depended on its arrival. For, like frost in October, the missionary barrel could be expected to come. It usually arrived around the first of October.

Yet my brothers and I began watching by the middle of September. Visualizing the treasures awaiting us, we hastened to meet Papa when he came from town.

"The missionary barrel!" cried Jim eagerly. "It didn't come today?"

"No, son," Papa answered patiently. "It's a mite early yet."

"Will it come next week then?" wondered Jerry.

"It might at that," replied Papa, his voice still conveying a patient note.

"Well, it will come soon," decided Clayton.

"Of course," agreed John wholeheartedly.

By Papa's side I walked in little hopscotch skips, my heart all tinglylike with a unique anticipation as I thought of the missionary barrel. The stored-up, tiptoe brightness would keep the rays inside me until the wonderful treasure came.

One year, however, despite anticipation, the missionary barrel failed to arrive at our home. Looking back at the memorable episode, Mama summed up the situation for all of us.

"A special blessing we received that year," she always said. "I'll never forget the time the missionary barrel was missing."

The time was a year when we'd moved from Deep Valley to a town beyond our hills, because Papa was going to college at last! When he and Mama married, both of them had only an eighth grade education. He taught a few years when he could get a school, but he spent most of his years farming. Then the kind people from the northern cities who started our little Presbyterian church encouraged Papa to go to high school. Since he had now received his diploma, they planned to help with his college education. These kind friends were the ones who'd been sending the missionary barrels.

"The missionary barrel may be late this year," Mama prepared us, soon after we settled in the new town. "But it will come, of course," she added assuredly.

As I sat reading a storybook that had come in the barrel the previous year, I sensed again the excitement of anticipation. The hopeful expectation brought back the glorious Christmas days we experienced each autumn in our Deep Valley home.

Actually, the "missionary barrel" hadn't been a barrel at all. Rather, it was a huge, bulky package which Papa brought from the post office. Mama had the barrel waiting, however. She and Papa carefully placed the items from the package in it. From that time forth, the round, wooden object became transformed into a wonder of radiance and treasure.

"A game of jacks!" Papa called, holding up a blue red box. "For you, Jenny?"

"Oh, no," I would answer, attempting to be unselfish, though much against my private wish. "My turn came first last year."

"For you then, Jerry-boy?"

"Oh, yes, thank you, Papa," replied my youngest brother. "I love jacks. But Jenny can play with them, too."

"Trousers!" announced Papa next. "They look too big for any of you."

"Never mind," said Mama blithely. "I'll stitch them over."

"And dresses. For you, Betsey, and Jenny."

"They won't fit either of us," discerned Mama quickly. "But just wait till I get my needle going!"

Yes, jacks, trousers, dresses, sometimes jackets or coats hardly worn, fragments of lovely material that Mama deftly made into garments or quilts, shoes, marbles, religious books for Mama and Papa—and last year, my wonderful Bible storybook! All these had been contained in the marvelous missionary barrel.

But now this year, our first in the new town far from the old home, the boys and I grew unduly apprehensive that the package might not find its way to us. And if it didn't, would we ever survive the cold months?

"It takes us through the winter," Mama had often reminded us.

Winter was not far away. October came with colored leaves and the first frost. November then crept in with dreary days.

"We'll not make it through the winter," I observed on a bleak November day, unable to withhold my fears another second. "With no missionary barrel, that is,"

"Never mind, Jenny," replied Mama, placidly darning the boys' socks. "Our friends have not forgotten us. And God is with us here, the same as He's always been," she affirmed.

"Why, there's Papa coming home!" I exclaimed happily, my faith quickly restored.

"Betsey," said Papa as he entered the door, "one of the professors says there's a family down the street whose name is Jennings. We should get acquainted."

"It would be nice to have some neighbors here," observed Mama quietly.

"Why, you've been lonely here, Betsey. And I hadn't even noticed! We'll visit the other Jennings family. They moved in last week, Professor Trimble said."

"They may be lonely, too," Mama said.

That afternoon we called on the family. We discovered a Mr. and Mrs. Wilfred M. Jennings and their eight children—five boys and three girls. When we entered the doorway, all eight of the children were sitting starry-eyed around a big package that Mr. Jennings was untying!

We looked at one another, all seven of us. Quietly Mama led us over the threshold.

Quietly, too, she led the way back across the threshold an hour later. Behind her, in the snow outside, Papa kept repeating in wonder, "Wilfred M.—William M., the two names aren't so different really. And we're both called Will! Names," he muttered in a low tone.

"Of course we couldn't tell them the package was actually ours," Mama pointed out to my brothers and me. "Not after Mr. Jennings kept murmuring the address. 'Mr. W. M. Jennings,' he read repeatedly."

"And he kept saying, too, 'Some kindhearted church folks must have heard we needed help,'" Papa remembered, his voice still low and tinged with awe. "Not for a moment did he consider the package might belong to us."

No, we couldn't possibly have told the family of their mistake. Not after the heartfelt gratitude of the father, the happy, grateful smile in the mother's eyes, and the excited Christmas spirit of the children. And most of all, not after the least little girl had clasped a brand-new Bible storybook in her arms, exclaiming joyfully, "A book about Jesus, Daddy, a book about Jesus!"

No, despite the storybook and all the remainder of the wondrous treasure that we had lost, not for anything in the world could we have mentioned the mistake. Because circumstances would have resulted in stealing happiness from someone else.

"Never can you steal happiness to hoard it for yourself alone. Only by sharing it with your neighbors can you keep it growing," Mama told us, as she watched the falling snowflakes on the street. As she opened the gate she added happily, "It did my heart good to see the joy of our new neighbors."

"Yes," said Papa quietly, watching the snowflakes, too. "And the Lord will make a way for us here, the same as He did back in Deep Valley. Most surely, God's blessings will continue with us always."

"Why, of course, Will," replied Mama quite matter-of-factly as she searched for the key to our door. "Only now we've received a marvelous blessing from the missing missionary barrel!"

# CHAPTER 13

# Mama's Kitchen Lamp

When Papa received his college diploma, we moved back to the land we loved. Once more we dwelt amid the loveliness of Deep Valley where we visited the neighbors and they, in turn, shared life with us.

Several new families had now moved among us. Mama lost no time in becoming acquainted with them. The twin brothers, James and Paul Harris, who shared our only sheet, liked our valley so well that they had returned with their mother. James married Mike Riley's second oldest sister, and Paul married Mona, the fifth daughter of old John Riley.

Since Papa now taught school over in Lonesome Cove, Mama, my brothers, and I attended to the evening chores. Never one to procrastinate, Mama believed in getting the work finished by dark. Unless something unforeseen turned up, she rarely needed to use the kitchen lamp at night. As a rule, she lighted it only on Friday nights.

On Friday afternoons Papa stayed late at the schoolhouse, attending to his school housecleaning. He washed the blackboards and cleaned his desk. With the extra work sometimes he didn't return home until sunset, or even after darkness had covered the hills.

When he rode his pony into the yard, Mama ran quickly to light the kitchen lamp. This was a signal to Grandma, whose house stood some distance from ours.

Grandma Jennings set great store on Papa, her oldest child. Even after he married and had a family of his own, she couldn't sleep unless she knew he was all right. She especially worried about him when he came home late. So she and Mama, who also worried about Papa, arranged the signal. When Grandma saw the bright glow from our kitchen lamp, she knew all was well and that Papa had come home safely again.

One night Mama delayed in lighting the kitchen lamp. At eight o'clock Papa still hadn't arrived. We sat around the hearth, listening for a sound, the sound of our pony lifting the gate latch as Papa had taught him to do.

As Clayton and I played checkers, I noted a puckered frown of anxiety above Mama's eyes. Just then we heard someone at the gate. It was Grandma, bundled up in an old brown overcoat. As she entered the door and dusted snowflakes from her faded shawl, she looked at Mama in a long moment of shared concern. "Betsey, hasn't Will come yet?"

"Not yet," Mama answered quietly.

"Then we're going after him!" declared Grandma.

"Naturally he'd be later with the snow blocking the hillside path," Mama replied in an uncertain voice.

"We're going after him," repeated Grandma with determination. "You and I, Betsey."

"We'll do just that," agreed Mama. "Something may be wrong, Now, Clayton—" she began, listing directions.

On her fourth admonition we heard the pony by the gate. Clayton and John ran out hurriedly. They returned

74

with Papa. Behind them came Mona and Paul Harris. Mona was crying, while Paul held her close.

Mama and Grandma, working side by side, didn't take time to ask questions. Instead, they ran efficiently here and there to hunt dry clothes and warm up the food.

After everyone had eaten, all of us sat near the fireside. No one seemed inclined to talk. Abruptly Mona spoke from her seat near the mantel.

"I couldn't help it," she said simply. "She drove me to it."

She meant Minerva Harris, of course. Only last week Mona and her mother-in-law had had a fresh quarrel. But what had Minerva driven Mona to do?

"We quarreled again," Mona continued tonelessly. Her voice was flat as the stagnant water in our pond by the barn. "Even after I'd made firm resolutions last week."

Paul attempted to comfort her. "Now, honey. Don't blame yourself so much."

"I know, Paul, but I've been at fault in more ways than one. After all, she is your mother and aging every day."

Mama looked tenderly at Grandma, and Grandma glanced intuitively up at her. A shared understanding of companionship passed between them.

Mona must have seen the look. With a nervous gesture, she began folding little pleats in her dress. "How do you do it?" she asked wearily. "I mean, how do you two get along so well?"

Mama smiled and glanced at Grandma again. "I don't really know," she answered slowly. "Well, perhaps I do, too. You see, we've got Will between us. We both love him. Also, there are the children and the kitchen lamp."

"The kitchen lamp!" exclaimed Mona. "That's what I missed tonight. After the quarrel, I looked up this

75

way to see its glow. You always lighted it on Friday nights."

She paused, pleating her dress again. "Somehow the flame in the window gave me faith to go ahead. But tonight the glow was missing and —I ran away."

Papa filled in the story. "Paul came to the schoolhouse, and we began searching for her. We found her in the snow."

We continued to watch the firelight. Paul spoke at last. "Mona, I'll build Mother a little house near the garden. She asked me to do so a while back. No kitchen was ever made large enough for two women."

"Oh, Paul," Mona said contritely. "I'll try harder from now on. Truly I will. I'll try hard to see your mother's side, too."

She turned to Mama. "Tell me, Betsey, what did you mean about the kitchen lamp? You said it was between you and Will's mother."

Mama and Grandma looked fully at each other. They turned to watch the steady flames reaching toward the chimney. "You tell them, Grandma," Mama said.

Grandma leaned back in the rocking chair. "It's quite a tale," she began. "When Betsey married Will, I was frightfully jealous. He was my oldest child and I'd always seen to him."

"And I was jealous, too," admitted Mama. "I thought she still meant to hang on to him."

Papa sat gazing at his left shoe, listening quietly.

"We didn't quarrel openly," continued Grandma. "Yet through the years little things' kept coming up. Double meaning words and sidewise looks. If you know what I mean. At last we had it then—our one and only battle. You tell the rest, Betsey," she said gently.

"It was about Will, of course," recalled Mama. "For once, we brought out all the piled-up resentments between us as we discussed our different feelings. And then we agreed that perhaps they were only natural after all. There was a wife's viewpoint, and a mother-in-law's. But that was after what happened to the Book."

"The book? What book?" asked Mona.

"The Bible lay on the stand table," said Mama in a low tone. "I was shouting out still more of my grievances when I turned and accidentally knocked over the table. The Bible almost fell into the fire."

"We caught it together," Grandma added, her voice a mixture of awe and tenderness. "It wasn't harmed. Betsey couldn't help it. I'd driven her too far. What might have happened sobered us both, I guess." She squeezed Mama's small hand between her wrinkled ones.

"We sat together on the sofa with the Bible between us," Mama remembered quietly. "After we had talked a long time, we read the Book of Ruth together. Things have been different ever since."

"We agreed on the lamp signal together then," Grandma continued, "not merely as a sign that Will had arrived safely home, but as a reminder that the true communication we had established between us was still burning brightly. The light was to be a symbol of the faith and trust and understanding necessary for Christian family relationships."

Mona's lovely youthful face showed strains of stress and unrest. "I'll try," she said again, turning to her husband. "I'll try to make things right for all of us."

"Try reading the Book of Ruth together," Grandma advised her gently. "And pray every day. You won't be able to do it on your own."

"We have the Bible Paul bought as a drummer boy," Mona remembered. "I'll read it every day now."

"I'll keep the kitchen lamp burning," Mama promised.

77

# CHAPTER 14

# Mama's Kitchen Rug

The linoleum rug, or what was left of it after serving countless footsteps, had faded to a pale mint green. The round designs of flowers, which had been a special delight to Mama when she first bought the rug from a garrulous salesman, were no longer distinguishable one from another. And the bare brown spots where the flowers had been rubbed out entirely Mama kept covered with gaily colored rag rugs.

When I returned home from school one day, Mama had washed the rag rugs, and they were drying in the sun. She had carefully mopped the green linoleum rug. Without the braided rugs the bare brown spots stood out here and there over the kitchen.

"Why, Mama, I didn't know we had that many spots!" I made hopscotch steps across them. "You need a new rug."

A dreamy look leaped like the flame of candlelight into her eyes, the type of look they held when she surveyed a room before cleaning it.

On Friday night after supper we sat around our

kitchen table. Papa read his farm magazine. Clayton and John were busy with their high school books, and Jim and Jerry studied history together. I sat reading *Little Women,* which had come from one of our missionary barrels.

Mama, in her rocking chair, mended the boys' shirts. Then she looked at the new catalogue. Again the dreamy look lay in her soft blue eyes.

"Find anything in the wish book, Betsey?" asked Papa, just before he reached for the Bible on the mantel.

"Oh, I was just wondering about a new rug. This one has taken many a footstep." Mama sighed as she closed the pages.

"Yes," Papa said, reaching his right hand to his chin in his thoughtful gesture. "Go ahead and buy a new rug if you want to, Betsey."

"Well—" Mama paused so long that I looked up from reading. I sensed a lost feeling for her because the dreamy look was now receding from her eyes.

"Gather up your books, boys," said Papa. "It's time for prayers."

Just before he opened God's Book, Mama finished her sentence.

"Not this year, Will," she decided. "Maybe next. The boys' books will cost a lot. Clayton needs a new jacket, and John's sweater is threadbare."

As Papa read, I sat still between him and Mama. His voice was like a song always, caressing words that dipped and soared and made you feel all choked up in your throat and sort of misty in your eyes.

This night he read about the refining pot for silver and the furnace for gold. I didn't know what a "fining pot" was, but I knew about Mama's pots and pans. Every Saturday she scrubbed them with fine sand until they shone clean. When Papa read of the furnace for gold, I remembered Daniel's friends in the fiery furnace; and the

79

gold made me think of lazy Dan Bender's hope of finding gold in our mountains.

"'Children's children are the crown of old men; and the glory of children are their fathers,'" read Papa from Proverbs. His hand reached to squeeze mine as his voice dipped down like the hidden ravine where I loved to play in my grapevine swing.

"'A gift is as a precious stone in the eyes of him that hath it: whithersoever it turneth, it prospereth,'" Papa read. The words sounded just like poetry. Papa had read poems to the boys and me as long as I could remember.

I thought of the oranges and bright red peppermint sticks I always expected in my black stockings at Christmas. I looked at Mama again and thought of her wish for a new rug. I glanced at Clayton, whom I loved the best of all my brothers, and remembered the old black jacket he'd worn the year before, also John's sweater which Mama had mended so often. Why, her doing without a new rug to buy a jacket and sweater for my brothers would be giving gifts to them. Was that what lay behind all gifts, I wondered—the doing without things yourself so you could give something to others?

That winter Clayton got a new jacket, and John received a beautiful blue sweater. They both hugged Mama when she cut the string from the mail-order package. When I reached up to feel the soft texture of Clayton's jacket, he stooped down and swung me high on his shoulder. From there I could look down on them all.

Mama would not get her new rug now because Papa couldn't have much money left, but she had that dreamy look in her eyes. He had bought new shoes for the younger boys and me, and the jacket and sweater must have cost many dollars. Was Mama beginning to feel dreamy about other things besides new kitchen rugs and how a room would look if she changed the furniture around?

The next spring I found out what had made Mama dreamy that day in December.

On a warm May evening when lilac blooms swayed against our doorway, Papa and Mama, John and Jim and Jerry and I sat in a row of special seats all trimmed in crinkly white paper up and down the sides. Above us, on long benches where people sat at ball games, were many strange persons. I asked Papa why they sat up there, and he told me they did not have any close kinfolk wearing the caps with the swinging tassels and the long, flowing gowns.

But we did. My brother Clayton would graduate from high school that night, and in a few moments he would walk across the stage to receive his diploma. When finally he reached out to receive the black, flat object, my heart was so proud I felt it would burst. At that moment Papa whispered across me to Mama, "Your kitchen rug, Betsey."

Mama smiled at him and somehow it seemed to me, squeezed there between them, that for that one moment they didn't see me or anybody else in all that big crowd of people.

I wondered about that and I thought, too, once more of Mama's kitchen rug. Abruptly I remembered that shivery December afternoon when the mail-order package came. Mama was looking forward to this night then, I knew, and dreaming how everything would look and feel—how tall and handsome Clayton would be in his cap and gown.

The next spring John walked across the same stage to receive his diploma. Again we sat in special seats.

"Your kitchen rug, Mama," I whispered, between her and Papa once more.

"What's she saying?" Papa whispered to Mama.

But I think he heard me, too. Mama looked queer for

a moment, and then I could have sworn that she and Papa exchanged the identical look which had passed between them the year before, the look that seemed to be shared by them alone.

John went to college with Clayton in the fall. In the summer the boys had dug herbs, sold berries, and hoed corn for Elijah Henson. At school they worked in the cafeteria.

At home we still stepped carefully back and forth across the old green kitchen rug and walked softly across the braided rag rugs. Since Papa was sick and unable to teach that year, Mama stacked the pantry shelves higher with canned foods. We placed other cans and churns of pickled beans and corn in the cellar. Also, we stored potatoes, turnips, carrots, and apples there, for with two boys in college and two in high school, Papa and Mama had to scrape every penny available to meet expenses.

Not for one moment, however, during those difficult years did I feel that our family might be sadly lacking in certain worldly goods. Always on our table there was an abundance of good, wholesome food we'd raised on the farm. And if my school dresses weren't always bright and new, well, my schoolmates wore faded dresses also. Our family was rich in our love for each other, and our home in Deep Valley was the loveliest spot in the world. We were rich in our faith in God, whom we stopped to thank each day for all the blessings He showered on us and for His care of the boys away from home.

Eventually Mama did acquire her new linoleum. Our corn crop turned out unusually large one year, and Papa bought Mama the most beautiful rug I'd ever seen. When the boys came home at Christmas, they thought so, too.

My mother did without many things to give gifts to those whom she loved. As the years sped by, I realized this truth with grateful thanksgiving. And on holidays or other special occasions when I prepared to wear a new dress she had made for me, I remembered Papa's reminding her at Clayton's graduation, "Your kitchen rug, Betsey."

Yes, throughout the years Mama passed up many luxuries she would have liked to own. And always, the phrase "Mama's kitchen rug" symbolized for me the sacrifices she made to mold her children into the type of Christian adults who would in turn do their part to leave the world a better place than when they entered it.

"A gift is as a precious stone in the eyes of him that hath it: whithersoever it turneth, it prospereth." Last night, in the new Baptist church on Pinnacle Mountain, brother John chose these words for his sermon text. He turned to smile directly at Mama.

My husband Stephen and I, along with Stevie-boy, sat in the back. From there I couldn't see my mother's face. Yet I knew with certainty that with John's smile, the old dreamy look had once more leaped like a candle flame in Mama's sky blue eyes as they reached up to John. She was thinking of Clayton teaching in a college far away, of Jim's pastorate in another state, and of Jerry's shining office in the town clinic.

# CHAPTER 15

# The Sale of Rose Petal

When Big Papa was killed by a falling tree as he cut timber, Mama comforted her mother. And when Papa died of a heart attack, we children knew that Mama needed help. As a family, we had learned to be aware of our interrelationships and our need for each other.

This morning I prepared to drive to town to see the doctor, also to get some medicine for Mama. As I opened the door, I observed that last night's cheerless world with its crisscross shivering rain and barren fields had overnight assumed a breathtaking loveliness beneath a spread of snow. It was a still, white scene that made me pause and with reverence sense anew God's creativity. A bright sun and blue sky bade me "be still, and know."

Driving into town, I recalled other wintry days similar to this one. And then in the waiting room I looked up at the snow scene in the large photograph on the wall— almost identical with the scene outside. In the picture snow lay in soft, heaped-up mounds, and beside a tall mound near a hemlock tree stood an old lady whose hair resembled the silvery whiteness of the snow.

On previous trips I had often whiled away moments by noting various reactions to that picture. Some persons did not so much as glance in its direction. A few eyed it with momentary curiosity. Yet there were certain people who studied it with an intuitive understanding of love and an awareness of beauty in the commonplace.

An elderly man beside me coughed into his handkerchief, and I remembered the year when Papa had been ill.

On a cold winter day Papa had finally admitted he would not be able to finish his teaching term. Since the first killing frost in October, he'd been sick with the hacking cough which had been with him since his seesaw fight with the influenza epidemic of 1918. The doctor had often warned that his lung condition might give him future trouble. Now it appeared that old Dr. Wainwright's prediction had come to pass.

"Slack down a bit there, Will," the doctor said.

"But how can I?" Papa asked wearily. "With three boys in college now, I must continue teaching. The farm won't pay for everything. Jerry now has enough credits so he could enter the second semester, too. But I don't see how he can just yet."

"Well, you could get a loan and buy a secondhand Ford. That would do away with riding horseback all those miles to school in the winter," Doc had retorted.

"And just how would I repay the loan?" Papa asked testily.

Yes, it was quite true that Papa did not have money to invest in a car, either new or secondhand. But also, he invariably shunned all "newfangled inventions," and the chief one against which he had especially declared a private war was none other than the invention that had made a millionaire of Henry Ford.

So Papa continued to ride his horse the 10-mile round

trip to school and back each day. But now we knew he would ride no more that year.

Christmas was just around the corner. Already Mama had baked huge stacks of fruitcakes to be stored on the pantry shelves. I'd cracked walnuts and hickory nuts for her after school. Mama had made other cakes, too, which I decorated with bright red cinnamon berries.

Together she and I had knitted socks for the boys and a warm muffler and heavy socks for Papa. Little Cousin Rell was with us that winter, and Mama had made a big stuffed rabbit for him from quilt scraps. Sending him down to Big Mama's on Saturdays to get the boy out of the way, Papa and I had made a sled for the little tyke. Uncle Bartley had given me a can of red paint, and I had really made a showpiece out of the little coaster.

On Saturday nights after Rell was asleep, Papa had taken a little wooden guitar from the closet and carved by the firelight. He used strands of wire from an old screen door for the strings. Little Rell set such store by music. Even as a five-year-old, he sang the hymns in church. He'd practiced singing "Silent Night" as a solo for Christmas.

I noticed, however, that my brother Jerry didn't sing at his chores as he used to do. Neither did he tease me as in former days, and he'd stopped playing checkers with little Rell. Mama was worried about him. I often saw her eyes on him when she knew he wasn't looking.

Jerry told our parents he really didn't wish to enroll in college until the next September. But we knew better— Papa and Mama and I.

"Uncle Bartley wants me to help around the store in January," Jerry said. "He may need me for a full-time worker by summer. Why, I may just end up going into the store business with him."

"And give up your dream of being a doctor?" Mama had asked, her blue eyes filled with alarm.

"Oh, well—" Jerry had answered dejectedly. His voice trailed out like our path to the barn gate.

The boys came home from college for the holidays. Clayton kept us laughing as he told jokes and lifted Mama high in the air under the mistletoe. John preached the Christmas sermon in our church on Christmas Eve. Jim sang a solo—"O Little Town of Bethlehem." I was one of the angels in the shepherd play, and Rell was the little boy left behind to tend the sheep.

On Christmas Day our hearts were overflowing and joyous as the family sat down to eat. Papa managed to say grace without coughing, but John read the Christmas story from the Bible. It was the first time I could remember that Papa had missed reading the story on Christmas Day.

Christmas night the whole family gathered around the hearth. The older boys were much concerned about Papa's illness and about the problem of Jerry's entering college. They discussed various ways each one could help. We lacked money, I knew, and other things also. But sitting there with our family in the firelight glow, I felt rich and warm inside, thinking of the Christ child and of God's goodness in bringing us together again.

The next morning our outside world looked miserable, begging for sympathy. Amid the mournful, persistent pattering of rain Big Mama, bundled up in an old raincoat, came to check on Papa. She and Mama had a long talk by the kitchen stove. I was reading in the little lean-to room and couldn't help hearing them.

"Well, Mama," my own mama said, "we're edged against the wall this time. None of the boys must quit college. I won't permit that. All three are barely squeezing by with their expenses, working part-time. We've still got a little corn money left and some of Will's last check. I'll be paid next week, too, for the Kentucky Garden quilt I pieced for Minerva Harris."

Big Mama rocked away, her lips held tightly shut.

"Well, Betsey," she spoke at last, "the Lord provides, one step at a time, for those who help themselves. Plenty there be suffering about us, you know, with the cold winds killing all the fruit last spring, the drought in the summer, and the mines shut down this fall. We've plenty of company in our distress if that's any comfort," she mused.

"Betsey," she said after a lengthy pause, "you go ahead and sell all the quilts you can. I've got a little egg money and a few sales in mind for decoration flowers. And, well—Jacob Trelawney stopped by last week. He wants to buy Rose Petal."

"Rose Petal, Mama! But you can't sell Rose Petal. She may be just a cow, but you know yourself you always treated her like your own children."

"Maybe I do, maybe I don't," Big Mama said. "Be that as it may, Rose Petal is up for sale. And the money she brings goes to Jerry, and Jerry alone. Why, don't you remember how he saved her that time after she had Butternut? None of the men could help her a mite, and there was little 14-year-old Jerry, who brought her back to life and made her want to live again."

By this time Mama's eyes were misting over. She looked out the window.

"Yes," said Big Mama, "Rose Petal goes and the money goes to Jerry. Sure, and I've got Lily Bloom left, haven't I? She and the other stock are more than enough to keep an old woman like me on the move."

"But why can't Jake take Lily Bloom? Mama, we can't let you do this for us. Will and I can manage somehow. We should be able to look after our own children."

"There are times for help and times to let folks tote their own burdens. My helping, you wait and see, will not be charity. In the years to come it will prove a sound investment and fall on fertile ground. Give Jerry a push to start him off, a dose of faith in himself, and I'll guarantee he'll make the future steps on his own."

"But, Mama—"

"Listen, child," my grandmother's voice grew soft and tender as the apple blossoms in May, "you accept God's gifts every day—the air you breathe, the sunlight rays, the rain for crops, and strength to work for your family. You accept God's greatest gift, His Son, whose birthday we celebrated yesterday. You've brought up your children to accept Him, too."

Mama's eyes filled with tears.

"Then why can't you let your own mother help along life's pathway when the climbing grows too steep to walk alone?"

Mama and my grandmother were silent for a long moment.

"Jake won't take Lily Bloom. He said he wouldn't buy a cow in this country unless it be Rose Petal." Big Mama's voice, spiced with a brisk note of pride, was back to normal now. "So Rose Petal goes tomorrow. It will never be said that a grandson of mine couldn't continue his education to become a doctor just because of a little matter like greenbacks blocking the path."

The next morning gave birth to a lovely, snow-wrapped world—our delayed Christmas snow, little Rell called it. Jacob Trelawney came to visit Papa; and when he left, Mama, Big Mama, and I walked down the road with him.

My grandmother didn't utter a word all the way to her house. But when Jacob led Rose Petal from the barn, she placed a hand on Mama's sleeve. She turned aside to wipe the tears away.

"Betsey," she said, "does Will have any more of those

picture rolls left in his Kodak box? Do you reckon you could take a picture of Rose Petal and me?"

"Good afternoon," a brisk, hearty voice interrupted my reverie in the waiting room. A tall figure in white picked up the list on his receptionist's desk.

"A most beautiful day, don't you think?" the doctor asked the crowd. "Our Christmas snow is not belated this year, is it?"

For a fleeting instant the young man's eyes turned to lock questioningly with mine.

"Mr. Linwood, first. Please follow me," said the doctor efficiently.

The tall stranger must be new in town. As he rose from his seat, he took a last lingering look at the picture of the snow scene and the silver-haired lady whose courageous, lined countenance nestled against the face of a cow.

"Doc," said the stranger, "that picture there, would you mind my asking about it?"

The doctor reached his long fingers to the picture. He straightened it a fraction of an inch.

Then proudly my brother Jerry told the stranger, "Mr. Linwood, you are now being introduced to my grandmother, Mrs. Elizabeth Texas Greenleaf Tanner. Because of her and her faith in me, because of Rose Petal, you are entering my office today. The sale of Rose Petal was my delayed Christmas gift."

On the radio a clear, young voice began singing "Silent Night." Outside the sun shone bright and glorious across the snow.

Jerry looked at me again. He closed the door behind himself and the stranger. So this was now the fifth time. Five persons had now asked Jerry about the picture. Each time the occasion had been on Christmas Eve.

# CHAPTER 16

# Mama's Mailbox Ministry

As Mama grew older, naturally she became less involved in the lives of others. When she developed Parkinsons' disease and arthritis, she could no longer run here and there helping people out. But she could still sit by her kitchen window, watch for folks passing by, and invite them in to share meaningful moments. She sat there often writing letters to us children, her neighbors, and friends far away.

When the telephone made its entry into our valley, Mama felt that God sent it for a special purpose. Now that she was in poor health, she used it to keep in touch with relatives and friends. She used it especially to encourage new Christians as they followed Christ. She and Minerva Harris, who finally accepted the Lord at the age of 76, sometimes called each other twice a day to share thoughts they had gleaned from their Bible reading.

"When Mr. Bell invented the telephone, God was looking right over his shoulder," Mama avowed. "The Lord most surely had older people in mind when He planned its invention. Just think how we can visit over the line and check on each other's welfare."

91

Mama kept in touch with her friends also through the rural mail route when it finally came. She delighted in getting any type of mail, even worthless advertisements. Just to have an envelope in the mail with her name on it meant something to her, and because she felt that way, she decided others felt likewise. So she began writing little notes to the neighbors, asking about their welfare, or sending get-well wishes.

Once Clayton laughed hilariously when he saw Mama sending a letter to a neighbor who lived almost in sight of her house. "Why, you could almost call to her door," he declared.

"Be that as it may," retorted Mama in her old spicy manner, "Eliza is sick and needs a special note of cheer just now. Sure, I can call her on the phone or even walk down to see her—which I intend to do the last of the week. But tomorrow when the mail runs, she'll receive my card and letter. The two may just speed her medicine along the right channel, you know."

I looked at Clayton and he smiled at me. We knew that Mama's mailbox ministry for friends and family had started a long time ago, years before the mailman collected her letters filled with lines of wisdom, quotations, and favorite Bible thoughts.

The small shelves over our beds served the purpose of mailboxes when Papa built our new house. When he went to town on Saturdays, he collected the Jennings' mail from the post office. Of course we received very little. But sometimes Uncle Nathan or Aunt Netha wrote from Chicago, as did Carl and Mary Higgins, who had taught Sunday school in our valley. Also, we had some distant cousins in Ohio. The boys and I sometimes answered ads in Papa's farm journals, and we looked forward to receiving answers.

If we weren't around when Papa brought mail for us,

he deposited the letters in our individual shelves over our beds. Papa said a person's mail was private, and each of us had the right to read it alone. Afterwards we could share it with the family if we wished, which we usually did.

Mama used our shelves to share confidences, faith, and direction with her children. When John needed help in overcoming his shyness, Mama often left little notes on his shelf.

"'Be strong and of a good courage, fear not, nor be afraid of them,'" she would quote from Deuteronomy. "'For the Lord thy God, he it is that doth go with thee; he will not fail thee, nor forsake thee.'"

Or she might add a lighter note by advising, "Laugh a bit now and then, son. Don't you know that even the sun smiles over God's goodness? Try imitating the sun at least once a day."

Once Clayton found this note on his shelf: "There are no crownwearers in heaven that were not crossbearers here below," Mama had quoted after hearing Papa read the line from Charles Spurgeon's life. Clayton needed the assurance just then when confronted with problems while teaching an unruly class of boys in Sunday school.

Jim's grades often dipped to a low ebb because he was occupied with acting the clown and entertaining his classmates. More than once Mama admonished him. "A velvet carpet isn't spread out for learning," she wrote. "Start using your steps, son, to climb the homespun path of plain perseverance."

When Jim took her advice and applied himself to study, he found this note from Mama: "God has two dwellings, one in heaven, and the other in a meek and thankful heart," she quoted Izaak Walton. "He's in my heart today, son. Your diligence has placed Him there."

Jerry at 12 was under conviction several weeks before he finally accepted the Lord. In that period Mama took time almost every day to leave a note on his mailbox shelf. She didn't pressure him to hurry his decision along, nor did she beg him to become a Christian. She merely made him know that she and the Lord stood by him all the way. Her private writing at that time perhaps helped him more than oral conversation.

Mama shared many confidences with me, her only daughter. She taught me the joy to be found in creating a home for loved ones, the delight sensed over completed beauty and order, and her life proved that a woman's place is ever a divine and glorious one.

"What would our menfolk do without us, Jenny?" she once asked in a gay tone as we worked in the kitchen.

That night I found the timeless words from Shakespeare on my mailbox shelf: "Women are the books, the arts, the academies, that show, contain, and nourish all the world."

Mama's heart reached out to nourish and enrich the lives of all her children. Her heart was filled daily with love which prompted thoughtful acts for the neighbors. When the home belonging to Jacob and Cynthia Trelawney burned, Mama invited them to stay with us.

"Why, you haven't visited us in ages!" she exclaimed, making the family feel at home.

Later we learned that the pair had been on the verge of separation when their house burned.

"I've always thought that your gay voice and merry ways waked Cynthia up to see Jacob's side," Papa told Mama when the Trelawneys became happy together again.

Mama's blue eyes grew thoughtful. "It was more than that, Will. You see, we studied the Bible together while she was here. And when they left and Cynthia bought eggs from us, I often put a Bible verse for the day on top of the eggs."

When Mama made a new dress or bonnet for the neighbors, she pinned a copied pithy saying of cheer or advice along with a favorite Bible verse on the completed clothing. The quilts she made for our family and others were gay with colorful patterns. And with red and blue yarn she sometimes stitched "God is love," "He careth for you," and "A stitch in time saves bigger holes." Or else she'd embroider, "One step taken makes the ladder easier to climb," and "Trust is the best investment of all."

It was comforting to sleep under such a quilt. Mama stitched the line about trust as an investment on a quilt she sold to Minerva Harris. Minerva affirmed that it played a major role in her conversion.

Papa laughed once when he found a quilt with the rhyme of "Pat a cake, pat a cake, baker's man" lying on his bed.

"Are we sleeping under that tonight?" he asked.

"Go ahead and laugh, Will." Mama laughed too. "No, I don't expect you to sleep under that quilt. I just laid it there to sew the last stitch. It's one I made for the nursery at church. The children need a quilt to sit on while listening to Bible stories. But do you also see that corner?"

In one corner of the quilt Mama had stitched carefully the chorus of "Jesus Loves Me."

Mama helped Milton Tanner see that Jesus loved him when she copied Bible verses and placed them on top of the apples Papa carried to the Tanners. She sent Bible verses concerning diligence and thriftiness to Dan Bender with the strawberries Papa gave the Bender children, attempting to lift Dan from his laziness.

Although Mama feared that Dan would always depend on Papa and Nathaniel Lane to provide strawberries for his family, she yet had faith when she sent him the Bible verse from Psalm 128: "For thou shalt eat the labour of thine hands; happy shalt thou be, and it shall be well with thee."

Yes, Mama shared much wisdom, faith, and love with everyone. Her inquiring mind that searched daily for truth held a store of thought that she attempted to apply to the appropriate occasion. She quoted the pithy sayings used by her mother and grandmother. She remembered the wisdom she'd read and lines from the books Papa read to her as she sat mending or churning by the hearth. But most of all, Mama used the wisdom and words of faith and love from the Supreme Book in her mailbox ministry.

That Book had taught Mama that all life comes from God and that heaven holds eternal life for the believer. She was ever a believer in God, the Bible, and the importance of witnessing to the neighbors.

Most surely, in heaven now Mama is tripping about and witnessing of God's love. And if it were possible to send a message from her eternal home back to Deep Valley, I'm sure it would be filled with descriptive phrases concerning the neighbors she is finding up there. If she were writing from a kitchen window in heaven today, the letter would contain assurance that God's love is all-powerful, is shining gloriously there, and still present in every earthly trial.

I almost looked for a letter from her on the shelf above my bed this morning.